# The Life Planning Workbook

*A hands-on guide to help parents provide for the future security and happiness of their child with a disability after their death*

## Disclaimer

This book is intended to provide accurate information. It is not intended, however, to render any legal, tax, accounting, financial or other professional advice or services. You should therefore use this book as a general guide only. In addition, this book contains information that was available only up to the time of printing. Laws do change with some frequency.

That's why you must discuss your estate planning with a qualified attorney and financial planner before relying on the information you may find here or anywhere else.

# •THE•
# LIFE PLANNING
# WORKBOOK

A HANDS-ON GUIDE to HELP PARENTS PROVIDE for the FUTURE SECURITY and HAPPINESS of THEIR CHILD WITH A DISABILITY AFTER THEIR DEATH

**L. MARK RUSSELL, ATTORNEY**
**ARNOLD E. GRANT, ATTORNEY**

AMERICAN PUBLISHING COMPANY

P.O. BOX 988 • EVANSTON, IL • 60204-0988

Printed in the United States of America

ISBN 0-9635780-7-3

First Edition

Design: Rivera Design & Communications

This book is available at special, quantity discounts for bulk purchases for sales promotions, premiums, fund-raising or educational use. For details, call 800-247-6553 or write to:

American Publishing Company
P.O. Box 988
Evanston, IL 60204-0988

# Table of Contents

# Table of Contents

INTRODUCTION ............................................................................................ 3

THE LETTER OF INTENT ........................................................................... 5

    Information About Parents ................................................................... 9

    Information About Children with Disabilities .............................. 12

    Information About Other Children ................................................. 15

    Other Relationships ............................................................................ 27

    Advocates ................................................................................................ 42

    Medical History and Care ................................................................. 47

    Housing ................................................................................................... 79

    Daily Living Skills .............................................................................. 82

    Education ................................................................................................ 87

    Day Program or Work ........................................................................ 89

    Government and Private Benefits ................................................... 91

    Leisure and Recreation ...................................................................... 94

    Religion .................................................................................................. 96

    Rights and Values ............................................................................... 97

    Final Arrangements ............................................................................ 100

    Additions/Revisions ........................................................................... 101

FINANCIAL NEEDS ANALYSIS ............................................................... 113

    Calculating Your Child's Financial Needs ................................... 114

    Chart One—Part One: Person with Disability—Monthly Income ............................ 116

    Chart One—Part Two: Person with Disability—Monthly Expenses ........................ 117

    Chart One—Part Three: Person with Disability—Monthly Expense Summary ........ 118

    Chart Two: Family Balance Sheet .................................................. 119

    Chart Three: Life Expectancy ......................................................... 120

    Chart Four: Starting Portfolio Needed to Fund Various Annual Expenses Assuming No Trustee Fee ............................ 122

    Chart Five: Starting Portfolio Needed to Fund Various Annual Expenses Assuming a One Percent Trustee Fee ............... 131

**PREPARATION FOR ATTORNEY MEETING** ............................................ **143**

    General Information .................................................................. 143

    Critical People ........................................................................ 147

    Disposition of Property ............................................................ 151

**ESTATE PLAN ORGANIZER** ................................................................ **157**

    Professionals to Contact In the Event of Death ............................ 159

    Final Arrangements ................................................................. 163

    Location of Critical Documents ................................................. 165

    Information Relating to Financial Assets .................................... 168

**APPENDIX ONE—SUPPLEMENTAL FINANCIAL NEEDS ANALYSIS FOR**
**FINANCIAL PROFESSIONALS** ........................................................ **207**

**APPENDIX TWO—FORMS FOR FUTURE FINANCIAL NEEDS ANALYSES** ............... **243**

# Introduction

THE LIFE PLANNING WORKBOOK

# Introduction

*THE LIFE PLANNING WORKBOOK* IS INTENDED TO enable you to help assure continuity of care for your child with a disability after your death. Our experience is that this involves planning in four major areas. First, it is necessary that you plan for your child's personal needs in all the major areas of life—such as future living arrangements, education, employment, medical care, and recreational activity. Second, you need to consider your child's financial needs. Third, you will need to prepare estate plans so you can leave your property to the right people, in the proportions that you want. If you intend to leave property for a child with a disability, it will generally be necessary to create a trust so as to permit proper management and avoid loss of government benefits. Finally, it will be necessary for you to organize all critical records relating to your child and yourself so as to permit continuity of care after your death.

The workbook has been designed as a hands-on approach that will accomplish each of these goals. By completing Part One, you will communicate critical information about your child to future caregivers in all the major areas of life. Part Two can be used to calculate your child's financial needs after your death. Part Three will save you time and money by enabling you to gather the information attorneys and other professionals will need to help you implement your estate plan. Part Four can be used to help you organize your records so as to maximize the quality of your child's life after your death.

*The Life Planning Workbook* can be used by itself, or in conjunction with our first book, *Planning For The Future*, which was designed as a comprehensive guide on available options for families with children who have disabilities in the areas of life and estate planning. Topics covered in *Planning For The Future* include:

- Life planning (options available to people with disabilities in the area of residential care, education, employment and social activity);

- Advocacy and guardianship (selecting future caregivers and establishing their legal relationship to your child after your death);

- Financial planning (maximizing government benefits and developing your financial plan);

- Legal planning (using wills and trusts to leave assets to your child without affecting your child's eligibility for often needed government benefits);

- Reducing estate tax and the cost of probate administration so as to avoid depletion of your estate after your death;

- Planning for your own disability (the use of powers of attorney and living wills and planning for the devastating costs of old age); and

- Income tax planning (planning to take advantage of the various income tax deductions and credits available to help defray the costs of families that have a member with a disability).

It is our objective to help you plan for the future of your child with a disability. We respect your efforts and challenges and wish you the best of luck. We hope you will be able to secure your child's future, and gain peace of mind for yourself.

**PART ONE**

# The Letter of Intent

THE LIFE PLANNING WORKBOOK

PART ONE

# The Letter of Intent

ESTATE PLANNING FOR FAMILIES WITH children who have disabilities begins at the most basic level. How can you, as a parent, be assured that your son or daughter will lead as full and complete a life as possible after your death? What can you do to make sure your hopes and aspirations are realized?

In this part we lead you through the process of developing your Letter of Intent, which is simply a way of communicating important information about your child to future caregivers, encouraging you, as a parent, to sit down and think about what you want for your son or daughter and, equally important, what your son or daughter wants for his or her self. This important information must be communicated to those who will have primary responsibility for your child's care after your death.

In most cases, the future caregivers will be relatives. But even if these relatives are very close to your child, they may not be aware of important personal information. For instance, do the future caregivers know all the pertinent information about your child's medical history? Do they know the names, addresses, and phone numbers of all the professionals who serve your child? Do they know the names of professionals who you think should be avoided?

Moreover, if these relatives die or move away, successor caregivers will need explicit information.

Although not a legally binding document, a Letter of Intent is an ideal format. It allows you to communicate your desires to future caregivers and therefore will prove invaluable to them. The letter assumes even greater importance if these future caregivers are out of state and do not see your child frequently, or if the ultimate caregiver will be a trust officer at a bank.

To write a Letter of Intent, just follow the guide contained in this part, which covers vital details about what works well for your child in all of the major life areas: residential placement, education, employment, socialization, religion, medical care, final arrangements, and so on. Flexibility is important, so there should be several prioritized options listed under each heading. Possibly you will want to add some categories of your own to those listed in the guide, and you should feel free to make any adjustments necessary to meet the individual needs of your son or daughter.

If both parents are living, one of you may want to do the actual writing of the Letter of Intent while both of you will want to sign it. The letter can be typed or handwritten. It isn't an essay for school, and perfect grammar, spelling, or style are not the point. Your major concern is to make sure that your child will have a happy and meaningful life. Write clearly enough so that anyone who reads the letter in the future will understand exactly what you meant.

We cannot stress too much the importance of reviewing the letter and making revisions as changes in your plans for your son or daughter arise. Each year you should take out the letter and review it to make sure it remains current. Choose the same date each year, perhaps your child's birthday, so you won't forget. Occasionally there will be a significant change in your child's life, such as a new residential placement or a bad reaction to medication, and the letter should be revised immediately if any such change occurs. Many people keep the letter on a word processor so changes can be made more easily.

The following material is only a guide to writing your Letter of Intent. It is a list of everything we could think of that parents might put in their Letter of Intent. Not every point will apply to your particular situation. Remember, the purpose of the letter of intent is to include personal information about caring for your child that you want to communicate to future caregivers.

# Letter of Intent

Written by _____ Date _____

_____
(Relationship to the person with the disability—mother, father or both)

## INFORMATION ABOUT

_____
(Father's name)

### GENERAL INFORMATION

Full name _____

Social security number _____

Complete address _____

Home phone number _____ Work _____

Date and place of birth _____

City/town/country where raised _____

Fluent languages _____

Religion _____ Race _____

Blood type _____ Citizenship _____

### MARITAL STATUS

Current marital status _____

Date and place of marriage _____

Names, birth dates and addresses of children of current marriage.

_____

_____

_____

_____

_____

If previously married, list names, addresses, phone numbers and birth dates of prior wives and children from previous marriages.

_____

_____

_____

_____

_____

## INFORMATION ABOUT

_____
(Mother's name)

### GENERAL INFORMATION

Full name _____

Social security number _____

Complete address _____

Home phone number _____ Work _____

Date and place of birth _____

City/town/country where raised _____

Fluent languages _____

Religion _____ Race _____

Blood type _____ Citizenship _____

_____
**MARITAL STATUS**

Current marital status _____

Date and place of marriage _____

Names, birth dates and addresses of children of current marriage.

_____

_____

_____

_____

_____

If previously married, list names, addresses, phone numbers and birth dates of prior husbands and children from previous marriages.

_____

_____

_____

_____

_____

_____

# INFORMATION ABOUT CHILDREN WITH DISABILITIES

_____
(Name of child with disability)

## GENERAL INFORMATION

Complete name _____

Name child likes to be called _____

Social security number _____

Complete address _____

Home phone number _____ Work _____

Height and weight _____

Shoe and clothing sizes _____

_____

Gender _____ Race _____

Fluent languages _____

Religion _____ Citizenship _____

Date of birth _____

Complications _____

_____

_____

_____

Birth weight and place of birth _____

City/town/country where raised _____

## MARITAL STATUS

List the marital status of your son or daughter. If married, list the spouse's name, his or her date of birth, the names of any children, and their dates of birth. Also list any previous marriages, as well as the names, addresses, and phone numbers for the spouses and children from each marriage. Comment on relationship of each with person who has disability.

_____

_____

_____

_____

_____

_____

## GENERAL INFORMATION

_____
(Name of second child with disability, if there is one)

Complete name _____

Name child likes to be called _____

Social security number _____

Complete address _____

Home phone number _____ Work _____

Height and weight _____

Shoe and clothing sizes _____

Gender _____ Race _____

Fluent languages _____

Religion _____ Citizenship _____

Date of birth _____

Complications _____

_____

_____

_____

Birth weight and place of birth_____

City/town/country where raised _____

## MARITAL STATUS

List the marital status of your son or daughter. If married, list the spouse's name, his or her date of birth, the names of any children, and their dates of birth. Also list any previous marriages, as well as the names, addresses, and phone numbers for the spouses and children from each marriage. Comment on relationship of each with person who has disability.

_____

_____

_____

_____

_____

_____

# INFORMATION ABOUT OTHER CHILDREN

## INFORMATION ABOUT

_____
Insert name of other child

Complete name _____

Address _____

Home phone number _____ Work _____

Date of birth _____

Comments on relationship to child with disability (if the relationship is not good, say so clearly so future caregivers will have this important information).

_____

_____

_____

_____

_____

_____

Marital status (include name of spouse if married) _____

Names, birth dates of children (your grandchildren) _____

_____

_____

_____

Comments on relationship of children and spouse with child with disability (if the relationship is not good, say so clearly so future caregivers will have this important information).

_____

_____

_____

_____

_____

### INFORMATION ABOUT

_____

Insert name of other child

Complete name _____

Address _____

Home phone number _____ Work _____

Date of birth _____

Comments on relationship to child with disability (if the relationship is not good, say so clearly so future caregivers will have this important information).

_____

_____

_____

_____

_____

Marital status (include name of spouse if married) _____

Names, birth dates of children (your grandchildren) _____

_____

_____

_____

Comments on relationship of children and spouse with child with disability (if the relationship is not good, say so clearly so future caregivers will have this important information).

_____

_____

_____

_____

_____

**INFORMATION ABOUT**
_____

_____
Insert name of other child

Complete name _____

Address _____

Home phone number _____ Work _____

Date of birth _____

Comments on relationship to child with disability (if the relationship is not good, say so clearly so future caregivers will have this important information).

_____

_____

_____

_____

_____

Marital status (include name of spouse if married) _____

Names, birth dates of children (your grandchildren) _____

_____

_____

_____

Comments on relationship of children and spouse with child with disability (if the relationship is not good, say so clearly so future caregivers will have this important information).

_____

_____

_____

_____

**INFORMATION ABOUT**

_____
Insert name of other child

Complete name _____

Address _____

Home phone number _____ Work _____

Date of birth _____

Comments on relationship to child with disability (if the relationship is not good, say so clearly so future caregivers will have this important information).

_____

_____

_____

_____

_____

Marital status (include name of spouse if married) _____

Names, birth dates of children (your grandchildren) _____

_____

_____

_____

Comments on relationship of children and spouse with child with disability (if the relationship is not good, say so clearly so future caregivers will have this important information).

_____

_____

_____

_____

_____

_____

**INFORMATION ABOUT**

_____
Insert name of other child

Complete name _____

Address _____

Home phone number _____ Work _____

Date of birth _____

Comments on relationship to child with disability (if the relationship is not good, say so clearly so future caregivers will have this important information).

_____

_____

_____

_____

_____

Marital status (include name of spouse if married) _____

Names, birth dates of children (your grandchildren) _____

_____

_____

_____

Comments on relationship of children and spouse with child with disability (if the relationship is not good, say so clearly so future caregivers will have this important information).

_____

_____

_____

_____

_____

_____

**INFORMATION ABOUT**

_____
Insert name of other child

Complete name _____

Address _____

Home phone number _____ Work _____

Date of birth _____

Comments on relationship to child with disability (if the relationship is not good, say so clearly so future caregivers will have this important information).

_____

_____

_____

_____

_____

Marital status (include name of spouse if married) _____

Names, birth dates of children (your grandchildren) _____

_____

_____

_____

Comments on relationship of children and spouse with child with disability (if the relationship is not good, say so clearly so future caregivers will have this important information).

_____

_____

_____

_____

_____

## INFORMATION ABOUT

_____
Insert name of other child

Complete name _____

Address _____

Home phone number _____ Work _____

Date of birth _____

Comments on relationship to child with disability (if the relationship is not good, say so clearly so future caregivers will have this important information).

_____

_____

_____

_____

_____

Marital status (include name of spouse if married) _____

Names, birth dates of children (your grandchildren) _____

_____

_____

_____

Comments on relationship of children and spouse with child with disability (if the relationship is not good, say so clearly so future caregivers will have this important information).

_____

_____

_____

_____

_____

_____

**INFORMATION ABOUT**

_____
Insert name of other child

Complete name _____

Address _____

Home phone number _____ Work _____

Date of birth _____

Comments on relationship to child with disability (if the relationship is not good, say so clearly so future caregivers will have this important information).

_____

_____

_____

_____

_____

Marital status (include name of spouse if married) _____

Names, birth dates of children (your grandchildren) _____

_____

_____

_____

Comments on relationship of children and spouse with child with disability (if the relationship is not good, say so clearly so future caregivers will have this important information).

_____

_____

_____

_____

_____

## INFORMATION ABOUT

_____

Insert name of other child

Complete name _____

Address _____

Home phone number _____ Work _____

Date of birth _____

Comments on relationship to child with disability (if the relationship is not good, say so clearly so future caregivers will have this important information).

_____

_____

_____

_____

_____

Marital status (include name of spouse if married) _____

Names, birth dates of children (your grandchildren) _____

_____

_____

_____

Comments on relationship of children and spouse with child with disability (if the relationship is not good, say so clearly so future caregivers will have this important information).

_____

_____

_____

_____

_____

# OTHER RELATIONSHIPS

List special friends and relatives that your child knows and likes. Describe the relationships. These people can play an invaluable role, especially if the trustee resides out-of-state.

## INFORMATION ABOUT

_____
Insert name of friend or relative

Complete name _____

Relationship to child with disability _____

Address _____

Home phone number _____ Work _____

Approximate year of birth _____

Comments on relationship to child with disability.

_____

_____

_____

_____

_____

Marital status (include name of spouse if married) _____

Names, ages of children _____

_____

_____

Comments on relationship of friend or relative's children and spouse to child with disability.

_____

_____

_____

_____

_____

_____
**INFORMATION ABOUT**

_____
Insert name of friend or relative

Complete name _____

Relationship to child with disability _____

Address _____

Home phone number _____ Work _____

Approximate year of birth _____

Comments on relationship to child with disability.

_____

_____

_____

_____

_____

Marital status (include name of spouse if married) _____

Names, ages of children _____

_____

_____

_____

_____

Comments on relationship of friend or relative's children and spouse to child with disability.

_____

_____

_____

_____

_____

_____

_____

**INFORMATION ABOUT**

_____
Insert name of friend or relative

Complete name _____

Relationship to child with disability _____

Address _____

Home phone number _____ Work _____

Approximate year of birth _____

Comments on relationship to child with disability.

_____

_____

_____

_____

_____

_____

Marital status (include name of spouse if married) _____

Names, ages of children _____

_____

_____

_____

_____

Comments on relationship of friend or relative's children and spouse to child with disability.

_____

_____

_____

_____

_____

_____

THE LIFE PLANNING WORKBOOK

**INFORMATION ABOUT**

_____
Insert name of friend or relative

Complete name _____

Relationship to child with disability _____

Address _____

Home phone number _____ Work _____

Approximate year of birth _____

Comments on relationship to child with disability.

_____

_____

_____

_____

_____

_____

Marital status (include name of spouse if married) _____

Names, ages of children _____

_____

_____

_____

_____

Comments on relationship of friend or relative's children and spouse to child with disability.

_____

_____

_____

_____

_____

_____

**INFORMATION ABOUT**

_____

Insert name of friend or relative

Complete name _____

Relationship to child with disability _____

Address _____

Home phone number _____ Work _____

Approximate year of birth _____

Comments on relationship to child with disability.

_____

_____

_____

_____

_____

_____

Marital status (include name of spouse if married) _____

Names, ages of children _____

_____

_____

_____

Comments on relationship of friend or relative's children and spouse to child with disability.

_____

_____

_____

_____

_____

_____

_____

**INFORMATION ABOUT**

_____
Insert name of friend or relative

Complete name _____

Relationship to child with disability _____

Address _____

Home phone number _____ Work _____

Approximate year of birth _____

Comments on relationship to child with disability.

_____

_____

_____

_____

_____

_____

Marital status (include name of spouse if married) _____

Names, ages of children _____

_____

_____

_____

Comments on relationship of friend or relative's children and spouse to child with disability.

_____

_____

_____

_____

_____

**INFORMATION ABOUT**

_____
Insert name of friend or relative

Complete name _____

Relationship to child with disability _____

Address _____

Home phone number _____ Work _____

Approximate year of birth _____

Comments on relationship to child with disability.

_____

_____

_____

_____

_____

_____

Marital status (include name of spouse if married) _____

Names, ages of children _____

_____

_____

_____

_____

Comments on relationship of friend or relative's children and spouse to child with disability.

_____

_____

_____

_____

_____

_____

**INFORMATION ABOUT**

_____
Insert name of friend or relative

Complete name _____

Relationship to child with disability _____

Address _____

Home phone number _____ Work _____

Approximate year of birth _____

Comments on relationship to child with disability.

_____

_____

_____

_____

_____

Marital status (include name of spouse if married) _____

Names, ages of children _____

_____

_____

_____

_____

Comments on relationship of friend or relative's children and spouse to child with disability.

_____

_____

_____

_____

_____

_____

_____

_____

**INFORMATION ABOUT**

_____
Insert name of friend or relative

Complete name _____

Relationship to child with disability _____

Address _____

Home phone number _____ Work _____

Approximate year of birth _____

Comments on relationship to child with disability.

_____

_____

_____

_____

_____

_____

Marital status (include name of spouse if married) _____

Names, ages of children _____

_____

_____

_____

_____

Comments on relationship of friend or relative's children and spouse to child with disability.

_____

_____

_____

_____

_____

**INFORMATION ABOUT**

_____
Insert name of friend or relative

Complete name _____

Relationship to child with disability _____

Address _____

Home phone number _____ Work _____

Approximate year of birth _____

Comments on relationship to child with disability.

_____

_____

_____

_____

_____

_____

Marital status (include name of spouse if married) _____

Names, ages of children _____

_____

_____

_____

Comments on relationship of friend or relative's children and spouse to child with disability.

_____

_____

_____

_____

_____

_____

**INFORMATION ABOUT**

_____
Insert name of friend or relative

Complete name _____

Relationship to child with disability _____

Address _____

Home phone number _____ Work _____

Approximate year of birth _____

Comments on relationship to child with disability.

_____

_____

_____

_____

_____

Marital status (include name of spouse if married) _____

Names, ages of children _____

_____

_____

_____

_____

Comments on relationship of friend or relative's children and spouse to child with disability.

_____

_____

_____

_____

_____

_____

## ADVOCATES

An advocate is a friend, relative, social worker or charitable organization that looks out for the interests of a person with a disability. Advocates lack the legal standing of guardians. See Part Three.

List the people, in order, who you foresee acting as advocates for your child after your death. Make sure you have spoken with them.

1. _____

2. _____

3. _____

4. _____

5. _____

If you have not already included information about any of your potential advocates, you should complete the following.

## INFORMATION ABOUT

_____
Insert name of potential advocate

Complete name _____

Relationship to child with disability _____

Address _____

Home phone number _____ Work _____

Approximate year of birth _____

Comments on relationship to child with disability.

_____

_____

_____

_____

_____

Marital status (include name of spouse if married) _____

Names, ages of children _____

_____

_____

Comments on relationship of potential advocate's children and spouse to child with disability.

_____

_____

_____

_____

_____
**INFORMATION ABOUT**

_____
Insert name of potential advocate

Complete name _____

Relationship to child with disability _____

Address _____

Home phone number _____ Work _____

Approximate year of birth _____

Comments on relationship to child with disability.

_____

_____

_____

_____

_____

Marital status (include name of spouse if married) _____

Names, ages of children _____

_____

_____

Comments on relationship of potential advocate's children and spouse to child with disability.

_____

_____

_____

_____

_____

**INFORMATION ABOUT**

_____
Insert name of potential advocate

Complete name _____

Relationship to child with disability _____

Address _____

Home phone number _____ Work _____

Approximate year of birth _____

Comments on relationship to child with disability.

_____

_____

_____

_____

Marital status (include name of spouse if married) _____

Names, ages of children _____

_____

_____

Comments on relationship of potential advocate's children and spouse to child with disability.

_____

_____

_____

_____

**INFORMATION ABOUT**

_____
Insert name of potential advocate

Complete name _____

Relationship to child with disability _____

Address _____

Home phone number _____ Work _____

Approximate year of birth _____

Comments on relationship to child with disability.

_____

_____

_____

_____

_____

Marital status (include name of spouse if married) _____

Names, ages of children _____

_____

_____

Comments on relationship of potential advocate's children and spouse to child with disability.

_____

_____

_____

_____

# MEDICAL HISTORY AND CARE

## DIAGNOSES

List the main diagnoses for your son or daughter's condition, such as autism, cerebral palsy, Down syndrome, epilepsy, impairment due to age, learning disorder, mental retardation, neurological disorder, brain injury, physical disabilities, psychiatric disorder, schizophrenia, depression, bipolar, other mental illness or an undetermined problem.

_____

_____

_____

_____

_____

_____

_____

_____

_____

_____

_____

_____

_____

## Seizures

Indicate the seizure history of your son or daughter: no seizures; no seizures in the past two years; seizures under control; seizures in the past two years, but not in the past year; or seizures currently. Does anything act as a "trigger" for increased seizure activity?

_____

_____

_____

_____

## Functioning

Indicate your child's intellectual functioning level (mild, moderate, severe, profound, undetermined, etc.).

_____

_____

_____

_____

## Vision

Indicate the status of your child's vision: normal, normal with glasses, impaired, legally blind, without functional vision, etc. List the date of the last eye test and what was listed on any prescription for eyeglasses.

_____

_____

_____

_____

## HEARING

Indicate the status of your child's hearing: normal, normal with a hearing aid, impaired, deaf, etc. List the type of hearing aid if relevant.

_____

_____

## SPEECH

Indicate the status of your child's speech: normal; impaired, yet understandable; requires sign language; requires use of communication device; non-communicative, etc. If your child is nonverbal, specify the techniques you use for communication. List types and model numbers of any helpful devices.

_____

_____

_____

_____

## MOBILITY

Indicate the level of your child's mobility: normal; impaired, yet self-ambulatory; requires some use of wheelchair or other assistance; dependent on wheelchair or other assistance; without mobility, etc. List type of wheelchair if relevant.

_____

_____

_____

_____

## BLOOD

List your child's blood type and any special problems concerning blood. _____

_____

## INSURANCE

List the type, amount, and policy number for the medical insurance covering your son or daughter. What is included in this coverage now? Indicate how this would change upon the death of either parent. Make sure you include Medicare and Medicaid, if relevant.

_____

_____

_____

_____

_____

_____

_____

_____

## OTHER COMMENTS

_____

_____

_____

_____

_____

_____

_____

## CURRENT PHYSICIANS

Name _____

Specialty/types of practice _____

Address _____

Phone number _____

Average number of visits each year _____

Total charges during the last year _____

Amounts not covered by a third party, such as insurance (including Medicare or Medicaid).

_____

_____

Important findings or treatment _____

_____

_____

_____

_____

_____

_____

_____

_____

_____

## CURRENT PHYSICIANS

Name _____

Specialty/types of practice _____

Address _____

Phone number _____

Average number of visits each year _____

Total charges during the last year _____

Amounts not covered by a third party, such as insurance (including Medicare or Medicaid).

_____

_____

Important findings or treatment _____

_____

_____

_____

_____

_____

_____

_____

_____

## CURRENT PHYSICIANS

Name _____

Specialty/types of practice _____

Address _____

Phone number _____

Average number of visits each year _____

Total charges during the last year _____

Amounts not covered by a third party, such as insurance (including Medicare or Medicaid).

_____

_____

Important findings or treatment _____

_____

_____

_____

_____

_____

_____

_____

_____

## CURRENT PHYSICIANS

Name _____

Specialty/types of practice _____

Address _____

Phone number _____

Average number of visits each year _____

Total charges during the last year _____

Amounts not covered by a third party, such as insurance (including Medicare or Medicaid).

_____

_____

Important findings or treatment _____

_____

_____

_____

_____

_____

_____

_____

_____

_____

## CURRENT PHYSICIANS

Name _____

Specialty/types of practice _____

Address _____

Phone number _____

Average number of visits each year _____

Total charges during the last year _____

Amounts not covered by a third party, such as insurance (including Medicare or Medicaid).

_____

_____


Important findings or treatment _____

_____

_____

_____

_____

_____

_____

_____

_____

_____

**PREVIOUS PHYSICIANS**

Name _____

Address _____

Phone number _____

Specialty/types of practice _____

Important findings or treatment _____

_____

_____

_____

_____

_____

_____

Explain why you no longer choose to consult him/her.

_____

_____

_____

_____

_____

_____

_____

THE LIFE PLANNING WORKBOOK

---

## PREVIOUS PHYSICIANS

Name _____

Address _____

Phone number _____

Specialty/types of practice _____

Important findings or treatment _____

_____

_____

_____

_____

_____

_____

Explain why you no longer choose to consult him/her.

_____

_____

_____

_____

_____

_____

_____

## PREVIOUS PHYSICIANS

Name _____

Address _____

Phone number _____

Specialty/types of practice _____

Important findings or treatment _____

_____

_____

_____

_____

_____

_____

Explain why you no longer choose to consult him/her.

_____

_____

_____

_____

_____

_____

_____

## DENTIST

Name _____

Address _____

Phone number _____

Frequency of exams _____

Special treatments _____

Best alternatives in case current dentist is no longer available _____

_____

_____

_____

_____

_____

Other comments _____

_____

_____

_____

_____

_____

_____

_____

## DENTIST

Name _____

Address _____

Phone number _____

Frequency of exams _____

Special treatments _____

Best alternatives in case current dentist is no longer available _____

_____

_____

_____

_____

Other comments _____

_____

_____

_____

_____

_____

_____

## NURSING NEEDS

Indicate your child's need for nursing care. List the reasons, procedures, nursing skill required, etc. Is this care usually provided at home, at a clinic, or in a doctor's office?

_____

_____

_____

_____

_____

_____

_____

_____

_____

_____

_____

_____

_____

_____

_____

## CURRENT MENTAL HEALTH PROFESSIONALS

Name of psychiatrist, psychologist, or mental health counselor _____

Address _____

Phone number _____

Frequency of visits_____

Goals of sessions _____

_____

_____

_____

What types of therapy have been successful? _____

_____

_____

_____

_____

_____

What types have not worked? _____

_____

_____

_____

_____

## CURRENT MENTAL HEALTH PROFESSIONALS

Name of psychiatrist, psychologist, or mental health counselor _____

Address _____

Phone number _____

Frequency of visits_____

Goals of sessions _____

_____

_____

_____

What types of therapy have been successful? _____

_____

_____

_____

_____

_____

_____

What types have not worked? _____

_____

_____

_____

_____

## CURRENT MENTAL HEALTH PROFESSIONALS

Name of psychiatrist, psychologist, or mental health counselor _____

Address _____

Phone number _____

Frequency of visits _____

Goals of sessions _____

_____

_____

_____

What types of therapy have been successful? _____

_____

_____

_____

_____

_____

_____

What types have not worked? _____

_____

_____

_____

_____

## PRIOR MENTAL HEALTH PROFESSIONALS

Name of psychiatrist, psychologist, or mental health counselor _____

Address _____

Phone number _____

Frequency of visits _____

Goals of sessions _____

_____

_____

_____

What types of therapy have been successful? _____

_____

_____

_____

What types have not worked? _____

_____

_____

_____

Explain why you no longer choose to consult him/her.

_____

_____

_____

## PRIOR MENTAL HEALTH PROFESSIONALS

Name of psychiatrist, psychologist, or mental health counselor _____

Address _____

Phone number _____

Frequency of visits_____

Goals of sessions _____

_____

_____

_____

What types of therapy have been successful? _____

_____

_____

_____

What types have not worked? _____

_____

_____

_____

Explain why you no longer choose to consult him/her.

_____

_____

_____

## PRIOR MENTAL HEALTH PROFESSIONALS

Name of psychiatrist, psychologist, or mental health counselor _____

Address _____

Phone number _____

Frequency of visits _____

Goals of sessions _____

_____

_____

_____

What types of therapy have been successful? _____

_____

_____

_____

What types have not worked? _____

_____

_____

_____

Explain why you no longer choose to consult him/her.

_____

_____

_____

## THERAPY

Does your son or daughter go to therapy (physical, speech, or occupational)? _____

_____

What assistive devices have been helpful? List types and model numbers if relevant.

_____

_____

_____

Has an occupational therapist evaluated your home to assist you in making it more accessible for your child? If so, requirements should be listed at page 81.

_____

## THERAPIST

Name _____

Address _____

Phone number _____

Purpose of therapy _____

_____

_____

_____

_____

## THERAPIST

Name _____

Address _____

Phone number _____

Purpose of therapy _____

_____

_____

_____

_____

_____

## THERAPIST

Name _____

Address _____

Phone number _____

Purpose of therapy _____

_____

_____

_____

_____

_____

## DIAGNOSTIC TESTING

List relevant information about diagnostic testing of your son or daughter in the past: the name of the individual and/or organization administering the test, address, phone number, testing dates, and summary of findings. How often do you recommend that diagnostic testing be done? Where?

_____

_____

_____

_____

_____

_____

## GENETIC TESTING

List relevant findings of genetic testing of your child and relatives. Also list the name of the individual and/or organization performing the tests, address, phone number, and the testing dates.

_____

_____

_____

_____

_____

_____

## IMMUNIZATIONS

List the type and dates of all immunizations.

| Type of Immunization | Date(s) |
|---|---|
| | |
| | |
| | |
| | |
| | |
| | |
| | |
| | |
| | |
| | |
| | |
| | |
| | |
| | |
| | |
| | |
| | |

## DISEASES

List major childhood diseases and the date of their occurrence. List any other infectious diseases your child has had in the past. List any infectious diseases your child currently has. Has your child been diagnosed as a carrier for any disease?

| Disease | Date |
|---|---|
|  |  |
|  |  |
|  |  |
|  |  |
|  |  |
|  |  |
|  |  |
|  |  |
|  |  |
|  |  |
|  |  |
|  |  |
|  |  |
|  |  |
|  |  |
|  |  |
|  |  |

## ALLERGIES

List all allergies and current treatments. Describe past treatments and their effectiveness.

_____

_____

_____

_____

_____

_____

## OTHER PROBLEMS

Describe any special problems your child has, such as bad reactions to the sun or staph infections if he or she becomes too warm.

_____

_____

_____

_____

_____

_____

## PROCEDURES

Describe any helpful hygiene procedures such as cleaning wax out of ears periodically, trimming toenails, or cleaning teeth. Are these procedures currently done at home or by a doctor or other professional? What do you recommend for the future?

_____

_____

_____

_____

_____

## OPERATIONS

List major operations and the dates and places of their occurrence.

_____

_____

_____

_____

_____

_____

_____

## HOSPITALIZATION

List any other periods of hospitalization your child has had. List the people you recommend to monitor your child's voluntary or involuntary hospitalizations and to act as liaison with doctors.

_____

_____

_____

_____

_____

_____

## DEVICES

Does your son or daughter need any adaptive or prosthetic devices, such as glasses, braces, shoes, hearing aids, or artificial limbs?

_____

_____

_____

_____

_____

_____

## MEDICATION

List all prescription medication currently being taken, plus the dosage and purpose of each one. Describe your feelings about the medications. List any particular medications that have proved effective for particular problems that have occurred frequently in the past and the doctor prescribing the medicine. List medications that have not worked well in the past and the reasons. Include medications that have caused allergic reactions.

_____

_____

_____

_____

_____

_____

## OTC

List any over-the-counter medications that have proved helpful, such as vitamins or dandruff shampoo. Describe the conditions helped by these medications and the frequency of use.

_____

_____

_____

_____

_____

_____

## BIRTH CONTROL

If your son or daughter uses any kind of birth control pill or device, list the type, dates used, and doctor prescribing it.

_____

_____

_____

_____

_____

## MONITORING

Indicate whether your child needs someone to monitor the taking of medications or to apply ointments, etc. If so, who currently does this? What special qualifications would this person need?

_____

_____

_____

_____

## PROCUREMENT

Does your child need someone to procure medications? If so, list the name, address and phone number of the person who will do so.

_____

_____

_____

_____

_____

## DIET

If your child has a special diet of any kind, please describe it in detail and indicate the reasons for the diet. If there is no special diet, you might want to include tips about what works well for avoiding weight gain and for following the general guidelines of a balanced, healthy diet. You might also describe the foods your child likes best and where the recipes for these foods can be found.

_____

_____

_____

_____

_____

_____

## OTHER COMMENTS RELATING TO YOUR CHILD'S MEDICAL CONDITION OR CARE

_____

_____

_____

_____

_____

_____

_____

_____

# HOUSING

## WHAT WORKS WELL FOR

_____
(Your son or daughter's name)

## PRESENT

Describe your son or daughter's current living situation and indicate its advantages and disadvantages.

_____

_____

_____

_____

_____

## PAST

Describe past living situations. What worked? What didn't?

_____

_____

_____

_____

_____

_____

## FUTURE

Describe in detail any plans that have been made for your son or daughter's future living situation. Describe your idea of the best living arrangement for your child at various ages or stages. Prioritize your desires. For each age or stage, which of the following living arrangements would you prefer? Options include: a relative's home (which relative?), supported living in an apartment or house (how much supervision would be needed?), a group home (which one and how large?), a state institution (which one?), a private institution (which one?), foster care for a child, adult foster care, parent-owned housing (how much supervision would be needed?), housing owned by your child (how much supervision?). Indicate the minimum and maximum sizes of any residential options you consider suitable.

_____

_____

_____

_____

_____

_____

_____

_____

_____

_____

_____

_____

_____

THE LIFE PLANNING WORKBOOK

## ADAPTATION

Does the residence need to be adapted with ramps, grab bars, or other assistive devices? If so, describe in detail what is required.

_____

_____

_____

_____

_____

_____

## COMMUNITY

List the types of places that would need to be conveniently reached from your child's home. Include favorite restaurants, shopping areas, recreation areas, libraries, museums, banks, etc.

_____

_____

_____

_____

_____

_____

# DAILY LIVING SKILLS

## IPP

Describe your child's current Individual Program Plan. The location of the actual plan will be listed in Part Four.

_____

_____

_____

_____

_____

_____

_____

_____

_____

_____

_____

_____

_____

## CURRENT ACTIVITIES

Describe an average daily schedule. Also, describe activities usually done on "days off."

_____

_____

_____

_____

_____

_____

_____

_____

_____

_____

_____

_____

_____

_____

_____

_____

## MONITORING

Discuss thoroughly whether your son or daughter needs someone to monitor or help with the following items: self-care skills like personal hygiene or dressing; domestic activities like housekeeping, cooking, shopping for clothes, doing laundry, or shopping for groceries and cleaning supplies; transportation for daily commuting, recreational activities, and emergencies; reinforcement of social and interpersonal activities with others to develop social skills; other areas.

_____

_____

_____

_____

_____

_____

_____

_____

_____

_____

_____

_____

_____

## CAREGIVERS' ATTITUDES

Describe how you would like caregivers to treat matters like sanitation, social skills (including table manners, appearance, and relationships with the opposite sex). What values do you want caregivers to demonstrate?

_____

_____

_____

_____

_____

_____

_____

## SELF-ESTEEM

Describe how you best reinforce your son or daughter's self-esteem, discussing how you use praise and realistic goal setting.

_____

_____

_____

_____

_____

_____

_____

## SLEEP HABITS

How much sleep does your son or daughter require? Does he or she have any special sleep habits or methods of waking up?

_____

_____

_____

_____

_____

## PERSONAL FINANCES

Indicate whether your son or daughter needs assistance with personal banking, bill payments, and budgeting. If so, how much help is needed?

_____

_____

_____

_____

_____

## ALLOWANCE

Indicate whether you recommend a personal allowance for your son or daughter. If so, how much? Also, list your recommendations about supervision of how the allowance is spent.

_____

_____

_____

# EDUCATION

## SCHOOLS

List the schools your child has attended at various ages and the level of education completed in each program. Include early intervention, day care, and transition programs.

_____

_____

_____

_____

_____

## CURRENT PROGRAMS

List the specific programs, schools, and teachers your son or daughter has now. Include addresses and phone numbers.

_____

_____

_____

_____

_____

_____

_____

## ACADEMICS

Estimate the grade level of your son or daughter's academic skills in reading, writing, math, etc. List any special abilities.

_____

_____

_____

_____

_____

## EMPHASIS

Describe the type of educational emphasis (such as academic, vocational, or community-based) on which your son or daughter currently concentrates. What educational emphasis do you think would be best for the future?

_____

_____

_____

_____

_____

## INTEGRATION

Describe the extent that your child has been in regular classes or schools during his or her education. What are your desires for the future? What kinds of undesirable conditions would alter those desires?

_____

_____

_____

# DAY PROGRAM OR WORK

## PRESENT

Describe your son or daughter's current day program and/or job.

_____

_____

_____

_____

_____

_____

_____

## PAST

Describe past experiences. What worked? What didn't? Why?

_____

_____

_____

_____

_____

_____

_____

## FUTURE

Discuss future objectives. Prioritize your desires.

_____

_____

_____

_____

_____

_____

_____

## ASSISTANCE

Indicate to what extent, if any, your son or daughter needs assistance in searching for a job, in being trained, in becoming motivated, and in receiving support or supervision on the job.

_____

_____

_____

_____

_____

_____

## GOVERNMENT AND PRIVATE BENEFITS

There are many different types of government and private benefits that assist people with disabilities. Some of the more common ones are Supplemental Security Income (SSI), Social Security Disability Insurance (SSDI), Medicare, Medicaid, respite care, child care, counseling, homemaker services, in-home nursing/attendant care, transportation, cash subsides/vouchers, peer networking, architectural modifications, utility subsidies, specialized clothing, and others.

Please describe these important programs.

### BENEFIT

Type of benefit _____

Description of benefit (including monthly amount if relevant) _____

_____

_____

Name of agency (public or private) _____

Address _____

Phone number _____

Contact person _____

### BENEFIT

Type of benefit _____

Description of benefit (including monthly amount if relevant) _____

_____

_____

Name of agency (public or private) _____

Address _____

Phone number _____

Contact person _____

## BENEFIT

Type of benefit _____

Description of benefit (including monthly amount if relevant) _____

_____

_____

Name of agency (public or private) _____

Address _____

Phone number _____

Contact person _____

## BENEFIT

Type of benefit _____

Description of benefit (including monthly amount if relevant) _____

_____

_____

Name of agency (public or private) _____

Address _____

Phone number _____

Contact person _____

## BENEFIT

Type of benefit _____

Description of benefit (including monthly amount if relevant) _____

_____

_____

Name of agency (public or private) _____

Address _____

Phone number _____

Contact person _____

## BENEFIT

Type of benefit _____

Description of benefit (including monthly amount if relevant) _____

_____

_____

Name of agency (public or private) _____

Address _____

Phone number _____

Contact person _____

# LEISURE AND RECREATION

## STRUCTURED RECREATION

Describe your son or daughter's structured recreational activities. List favorite activities and the favorite people involved in each activity.

_____

_____

_____

_____

_____

_____

_____

## UNSTRUCTURED ACTIVITIES

What are your child's favorite means of self-expression, interests, and skills (going to movies, listening to music, dancing, collecting baseball cards, painting, bowling, riding a bicycle, roller skating, etc.)? List the favorite people involved in each activity.

_____

_____

_____

_____

_____

_____

## VACATIONS

Describe your son or daughter's favorite vacations. Who organizes them? How often do they occur, and when are they usually scheduled?

_____

_____

_____

_____

_____

_____

_____

_____

## FITNESS

If your son or daughter participates in a fitness program, please describe the type of program, as well as details about where and when it takes place and who oversees it.

_____

_____

_____

_____

_____

_____

# RELIGION

## FAITH

List the religion of your son or daughter, if any. Indicate any membership in a particular church or synagogue.

_____

_____

_____

_____

## CLERGY

List any ministers, priests, or rabbis familiar with your son or daughter. Include the names of the churches or synagogues involved and their addresses and phone numbers. Also indicate how often your child might like to be visited by these people.

_____

_____

_____

_____

## PARTICIPATION

Estimate how frequently your son or daughter would like to participate in services and other activities of the church or synagogue. Indicate how this might change over time. Also describe any major, valued events in the past.

_____

_____

_____

# RIGHTS AND VALUES

Please list the rights and values that should be accorded your son or daughter. Here are some examples of what you might list.

- To be free from harm, physical restraint, isolation, abuse, and excessive medication.

- To refuse behavior modification techniques that cause pain.

- To have age-appropriate clothing and appearance.

- To have staff, if any, demonstrate respect and caring and to refrain from using demeaning language.

_____

_____

_____

_____

_____

_____

_____

_____

_____

_____

_____

Give an overview of your child's life and your feelings and vision about the future.

_____

_____

_____

_____

_____

_____

_____

_____

_____

_____

_____

_____

_____

_____

_____

_____

Describe anything else future caregivers and friends should know about your son or daughter.

_____

_____

_____

_____

_____

_____

_____

_____

_____

_____

_____

_____

_____

_____

_____

_____

# FINAL ARRANGEMENTS

Describe any arrangements that have been made for your child's funeral and burial. List the full names of companies or individuals, their addresses, and phone numbers. Also list all payments made and specify what is covered.

_____

_____

_____

_____

_____

In the absence of specific arrangements, indicate your preferences for cremation or burial. Should there be a church service? If the preference is for burial, what is the best site? Should there be a monument? If cremation is the choice, what should be done with the remains?

_____

_____

_____

_____

_____

_____

# ADDITIONS/REVISIONS

# ADDITIONS/REVISIONS

_____

_____

_____

_____

_____

_____

_____

_____

_____

_____

_____

_____

_____

_____

_____

_____

_____

## ADDITIONS/REVISIONS

# ADDITIONS/REVISIONS

THE LIFE PLANNING WORKBOOK

# ADDITIONS/REVISIONS

# ADDITIONS/REVISIONS

_____

_____

_____

_____

_____

_____

_____

_____

_____

_____

_____

_____

_____

_____

_____

_____

_____

_____

# ADDITIONS/REVISIONS

# ADDITIONS/REVISIONS

---

---

---

---

---

---

---

---

---

---

---

---

---

---

---

---

---

THE LIFE PLANNING WORKBOOK

# ADDITIONS/REVISIONS

## ADDITIONS/REVISIONS

_____

_____

_____

_____

_____

_____

_____

_____

_____

_____

_____

_____

_____

_____

_____

PART TWO

# Financial Needs Analysis

# Financial Needs Analysis

THE LIFE PLAN FOR MOST PEOPLE WITH DIS-abilities involves the creation of a trust. In general, a trust is a legal relationship under which property is held, managed, and owned by a person or institution (the trustee) for the benefit of those persons for whom the trust was created (the beneficiary). In the case of families who have a child with a disability, parents will generally create a trust, naming the child with a disability as beneficiary and trusted friends, family members, or institutions as trustee. This enables parents to leave money for the benefit of the child in a form that permits effective management and control. For a complete discussion of trusts, including how to structure them so as not to reduce your child's government benefits, you may want to refer to our other book, *Planning For The Future*.

In this part we will give you the tools you need to calculate your child's lifetime financial needs, and how much must go in the trust to fund those needs. This is not to say that the amount you leave in trust should necessarily equal the amount you calculate to be required to meet your child's financial needs. None of us are omniscient; the calculations can be only estimates. It is possible that your child's financial needs will grow in the future or that government benefits your child relies upon will be reduced. Either circumstance would likely result in a substantial increase in your child's need for private funds. Similarly, your child may have access to other funds, such as a settlement from a personal injury claim. This would reduce the need for funds.

Moreover, if you have other children, you will want to be fair to them as well. This is particularly true if your other children will be expected to act as their sibling's advocate in the future. You will not want to create a resentment that could affect a brother or sister's willingness to be helpful. In fact, when parents do decide to leave a disproportionate share of their estate to a child with a disability, we frequently advise the parents to explain their reasoning to their other children in order to avoid resentment. Some parents leave an explanatory note in their Letter of Intent.

Calculating your child's financial requirements can, however, be quite instructive. It not only gives you a sense of what your child will need when you are gone, but it also helps shape your decisions regarding the disposition of your estate and helps you to decide among various investment alternatives. For example, if you find that your estate will not be sufficient to meet your child's needs, you may decide to purchase additional life insurance.

One mistake to avoid. Some parents disinherit a child with a disability, leaving everything to other children with the informal understanding that the other children will look out for their sibling. This can be a disastrous choice.

The relative who receives the extra money to look after the person with a disability might enter a nursing home and be required by the government to spend the money on his or her own care. The person might go bankrupt and be required to give the money to creditors, or get a divorce and be required to split the money with his or her spouse, or die and will the money to others, or simply refuse to spend it on the person with a disability.

It is far better to leave money in trust for the child who has the disability so that a separate fund of guaranteed money is available to the person who really needs it.

## CALCULATING YOUR CHILD'S FINANCIAL NEEDS

The process is less mysterious than it sounds. Begin by simply calculating the amount you currently spend on your child over and above government benefits. If your child is very young, you will need to estimate what you will be spending when your child is older. You then have to build in a reserve to pay for things that you currently do for free, but which your child may need to pay for after you have died.

The following are examples of some of the major items you will want to think about:

- **Advocacy and guardianship costs.** Will your child need the services of a professional advocate? If so, you will need to include the cost. If your child will rely on family members, will you want to reimburse them for their time? If not, how about their expenses? For example, a brother or sister may need to travel to visit a sibling; you may want them to be reimbursed for gas or airfare. Such payments may encourage a sibling to take the responsibility more seriously.

- **Emergency expenses for medical needs.** What kind of reserve will you need to provide for emergency medical and dental needs? Dental care can be a major expense. In some states, Medicaid does not pay the cost of dental care, and adults can incur substantial expenses for items such as root canals, crowns, or periodontal work.

- **Capital items.** Here we mean infrequent big-ticket items such as a television, VCR, a CD player, or some nice furniture.

- **Government benefits.** Obviously, your child's requirements will be significantly greater if your child does not receive government benefits such as social security, supplemental security income, medicaid, medicare, or state residential cost of care benefit programs. Even if your child does rely on such programs, you may want a reserve in case these programs are reduced in the future. Many families compute the reserve by going through the calculation described in the following pages twice, once assuming government benefits continue at the current level and again assuming such benefits are reduced or eliminated. Although it is unusual for a family to be able to fund the trust assuming no government benefits, the calculation can be educational.

To complete your financial needs analysis, just complete the forms that follow. The first chart, which contains three parts, enables you to calculate your child's anticipated annual income requirements. Charts Three, Four and Five can then be used to calculate the amount required by the trust to fund those needs. Chart Two is a simple balance sheet. You can use it to calculate your net worth so you can see whether the amount you intend to leave for your child will be sufficient to meet his or her needs. If not, you can consider buying additional life insurance.

The calculations are not entirely exact, because we are necessarily required to make certain assumptions about inflation, interest rates and tax rates. The charts assume a 6.5 percent rate of return on money contributed to the trust, a four percent inflation rate, and a twenty percent tax on trust income. The 6.5 percent rate of return represents the historic rate earned on taxable bonds, and the four percent inflation rate is also historically accurate. Although it is possible that the money you place in trust will earn more or less than 6.5 percent, or that our assumptions as to inflation will prove inaccurate, the assumptions seem reasonable.

The twenty percent tax rate also represents our judgment as to what is reasonable. In truth, the tax rate applicable to any trust which you create will depend on the amount of the trust's income and deductions. For example, if the trust pays substantial medical expenses for your child, it is possible that the trust will pay no tax at all because medical expenses are deductible for income tax purposes. The trust can also eliminate tax by investing in municipal bonds, though these tend to have a lower rate of return than taxable bonds. Moreover, it is possible that tax rates will change in the future.

The examples below illustrate how you can use the charts to calculate your child's financial needs. If you are interested in the results when we make different assumptions about tax rates and rates of return, you should refer to the charts and explanatory notes in Appendix One. The information contained in Appendix One is complicated and is probably unnecessary for most families. We include it only for the sake of completeness, and as a resource for financial professionals and others who are expert in financial matters.

It is advisable that you redo the calculations periodically, because your child's needs change over time. For example, if you do the calculations when your child is five, you will likely be interested in the amount required to meet your child's needs for 85 years, 90 years if your child is female. This is because the life expectancy of a 5 year old is 74 years if the child is male and 79 years if the child is female. However, by definition, 50 percent of the people outlive their life expectancy and it is therefore advisable for you to plan that your child will outlive his or her life expectancy by ten or more years. On the other hand, if you redo the calculations when your child is 20, your child's life expectancy will be less so fewer funds are required. Additional forms for recalculating your child's financial needs are provided in Appendix Two.

### Example One

John and Mary complete parts one, two and three of Chart One and determine that their 39-year-old son, Sam, will need $250 per month to fund his needs over and above that which is provided by the government. This figure is multiplied by 12 to get Sam's annual needs—$3,000. John and Mary are not concerned about trust administration fees because they trust Sam's sister to handle his finances.

John and Mary then go to Chart Three and determine that as a 39-year-old male, Sam has a life expectancy of another 41 years. They add ten years to Sam's life expectancy and then go to the column on Chart Four for life expectancy of 51 years, read over to the second row, which assumes required annual expenses of $3,000, and determine

that the trust must have an initial balance of $110,736 if it is to provide John with $3,000 per year for 51 years. (See chart, pg. 123.)

What if Sam needed $10,000 per year? As you can see from Chart Four, $369,121 would last 51 years. (See chart, pg. 126.)

If Sam needed $26,000 per year (perhaps because he did not receive government benefits), a little multiplication is necessary because the chart does not have a column for $26,000. Unfortunately, there was not enough paper for us to list every possibility.

John and Mary would go to the column for annual expenses of $1,000 and multiply by 26. Thus, if we continue to assume a life expectancy of 51 years, and if we also assume no administration fee, John and Mary would see from Chart Four that $36,912 must go into the trust if it is to provide Sam with $1,000 per year for his life. So to provide $26,000 per year, the trust would need $959,712 ($36,912 times 26).

Depending on the nature of Sam's disability, it would be possible that he would have a reduced life expectancy. John and Mary could likely find this out from Sam's doctor. In such a case, they could use the reduced life expectancy for the calculations, though it would still be advisable to assume that Sam would live several years beyond his life expectancy.

### Example Two

The facts are the same as in example one, except John and Mary decide they need a professional trustee such as a bank to manage Sam's funds. John and Mary go through the same methodology as example one, except they use Chart Five instead of Chart Four. Chart Five makes the same assumptions relating to inflation, tax rates and interest rates, except it assumes a 1 percent trustee fee, which is a typical bank charge.

Thus, if we assume a life expectancy for Sam of 51 years, Sam would need $140,003 to provide $3,000 per year. If Sam needs $10,000 per year, the amount required is $466,677. (See chart, pgs. 132 and 135.)

# CHART ONE—PART ONE
# PERSON WITH DISABILITY—MONTHLY INCOME

| Source of Income | Monthly Amount |
|---|---|
| **Employment** | $ _____ |
| **Government Benefits** | $ _____ |
| SSI | $ _____ |
| SSDI | $ _____ |
| Survivors | $ _____ |
| SSA Retirement | $ _____ |
| State | $ _____ |
| County | $ _____ |
| Other | $ _____ |
| **Other Sources** | |
| 1. _____ | $ _____ |
| 2. _____ | $ _____ |
| 3. _____ | $ _____ |
| 4. _____ | $ _____ |
| 5. _____ | $ _____ |
| **Total** | $ |

# CHART ONE—PART TWO

## PERSON WITH DISABILITY—MONTHLY EXPENSES

$ _____ **Housing**

_____ Rent/Month

_____ Utilities

_____ Maintenance

_____ Cleaning Items

_____ Laundry costs

_____ Other

$ _____ **Care Assistance**

_____ Live-in

_____ Respite

_____ Custodial

_____ Guardianship/Advocacy (approx. $50-$75 per hr.)

_____ Other

$ _____ **Food**

_____ Meals, snacks-home

_____ Outside of home

_____ Special foods/ gastric tube

_____ Other

$ _____ **Clothing**

$ _____ **Furniture**

$ _____ **Medical/Dental Care**

_____ General medical/ dental visits

_____ Therapy

_____ Nursing services

_____ Meals of attendants

_____ Evaluations

_____ Transportation

_____ Medications

_____ Other

$ _____ **Insurance**

_____ Medical/Dental

_____ Burial

_____ Car

_____ Housing/Rental

_____ Other

$ _____ **Automobile**

_____ Payments

_____ Gas, Oil, Maintenance

_____ Other

$ _____ **Recreation**

_____ Sports

_____ Special Olympics

_____ Spectator Sports

_____ Vacations

_____ TV/VCR

_____ Summer Camp

_____ Transportation costs

_____ Other

$ _____ **Education, Training, Etc.**

_____ Transportation

_____ Fees

_____ Books

_____ Other

$ _____ **Employment**

_____ Transportation

_____ Workshop fees

_____ Attendant

_____ Training

_____ Other

$ _____ **Personal Needs**

_____ Haircuts, Beauty Shop

_____ Telephone

_____ Cigarettes

_____ Church/Temple Expenses

_____ Hobbies

_____ Books, Magazines, Etc.

_____ Allowance

_____ Other

$ _____ **Special Equipment**

_____ Environmental control

_____ Elevator

_____ Repair of equipment

_____ Computer

_____ Audio books

_____ Ramp

_____ Guide dog/other special animals

_____ Technical instruction

_____ Wheelchair

_____ Other

$ _____ **Total Monthly Expenses**

# CHART ONE—PART THREE
## PERSON WITH DISABILITY—MONTHLY EXPENSE SUMMARY

| Monthly Expense Summary | |
|---|---|
| 1. Total Monthly Expenses (from page 117) | _____ |
| 2. Total Monthly Income (from page 116) | _____ |
| 3. Total Supplementary Funds Required (1 minus 2) | _____ |
| 4. Reserve in case of Government Benefit Reduction | _____ |
| 5. Total (3 plus 4) | _____ |

# FAMILY BALANCE SHEET

| Assets | Joint | Father | Mother |
|---|---|---|---|
| Residence | $ _____ | _____ | _____ |
| Other real estate | $ _____ | _____ | _____ |
| Bank accounts | $ _____ | _____ | _____ |
| Retirement accounts | $ _____ | _____ | _____ |
| CD's | $ _____ | _____ | _____ |
| Annuities | $ _____ | _____ | _____ |
| Stocks, securities | $ _____ | _____ | _____ |
| Business interests | $ _____ | _____ | _____ |
| Other assets | $ _____ | _____ | _____ |
| **Liabilities** | | | |
| Mortgage debt | $ _____ | _____ | _____ |
| Other debt | $ _____ | _____ | _____ |

**Current Family Net Worth** (current assets less current liabilities)          $ _____

| Life Insurance | Joint | Father | Mother |
|---|---|---|---|
| Death benefit | $ _____ | _____ | _____ |
| Premiums | $ _____ | _____ | _____ |
| Cash value | $ _____ | _____ | _____ |
| **Potential Inheritances** | $ _____ | _____ | _____ |

**Future Expectancies** (death benefits plus inheritances)          $ _____

**Total** (current family net worth plus future expectancies)          $ _____

# CHART THREE

## LIFE EXPECTANCY

| | Remaining Years Of Expected Life | | | | Remaining Years Of Expected Life | |
|---|---|---|---|---|---|---|
| Current Age | Male | Female | | Current Age | Male | Female |
| 5 | 74 | 79 | | 23 | 57 | 62 |
| 6 | 73 | 78 | | 24 | 56 | 61 |
| 7 | 72 | 77 | | 25 | 55 | 60 |
| 8 | 71 | 76 | | 26 | 54 | 59 |
| 9 | 70 | 75 | | 27 | 53 | 58 |
| 10 | 69 | 74 | | 28 | 52 | 57 |
| 11 | 68 | 73 | | 29 | 51 | 56 |
| 12 | 67 | 72 | | 30 | 50 | 55 |
| 13 | 66 | 71 | | 31 | 49 | 54 |
| 14 | 65 | 70 | | 32 | 48 | 53 |
| 15 | 64 | 69 | | 33 | 47 | 52 |
| 16 | 63 | 68 | | 34 | 46 | 51 |
| 17 | 62 | 67 | | 35 | 45 | 50 |
| 18 | 62 | 67 | | 36 | 44 | 49 |
| 19 | 60 | 66 | | 37 | 43 | 48 |
| 20 | 60 | 65 | | 38 | 42 | 47 |
| 21 | 59 | 64 | | 39 | 41 | 46 |
| 22 | 58 | 63 | | 40 | 40 | 45 |

*Chart Three is continued on next page*

# LIFE EXPECTANCY (CONTINUED)

| Current Age | Remaining Years Of Expected Life | |
| --- | --- | --- |
| | Male | Female |
| 41 | 39 | 44 |
| 42 | 38 | 43 |
| 43 | 37 | 42 |
| 44 | 36 | 41 |
| 45 | 36 | 40 |
| 46 | 35 | 39 |
| 47 | 34 | 38 |
| 48 | 33 | 37 |
| 49 | 32 | 36 |
| 50 | 31 | 35 |
| 51 | 30 | 35 |
| 52 | 29 | 34 |
| 53 | 29 | 33 |
| 54 | 28 | 32 |
| 55 | 27 | 31 |
| 56 | 26 | 30 |
| 57 | 25 | 29 |
| 58 | 24 | 28 |

| Current Age | Remaining Years Of Expected Life | |
| --- | --- | --- |
| | Male | Female |
| 59 | 22 | 27 |
| 60 | 23 | 26 |
| 61 | 22 | 25 |
| 62 | 21 | 25 |
| 63 | 20 | 24 |
| 64 | 19 | 23 |
| 65 | 19 | 22 |
| 66 | 18 | 21 |
| 67 | 17 | 20 |
| 68 | 16 | 19 |
| 69 | 16 | 19 |
| 70 | 15 | 18 |

FINANCIAL NEEDS ANALYSIS

# Starting Portfolio Needed to Fund Various Annual Expenses Assuming No Trustee Fee

| Life Expectancies | Annual Expenses $1,000 | $2,000 | $3,000 | $4,000 | $5,000 | $6,000 | $7,000 | $8,000 | $9,000 |
|---|---|---|---|---|---|---|---|---|---|
| 1 | $951 | $1,901 | $2,852 | $3,802 | $4,753 | $5,703 | $6,654 | $7,605 | $8,555 |
| 2 | $1,890 | $3,781 | $5,671 | $7,561 | $9,451 | $11,342 | $13,232 | $15,122 | $17,013 |
| 3 | $2,819 | $5,639 | $8,458 | $11,277 | $14,097 | $16,916 | $19,735 | $22,554 | $25,374 |
| 4 | $3,738 | $7,475 | $11,213 | $14,951 | $18,689 | $22,426 | $26,164 | $29,902 | $33,639 |
| 5 | $4,646 | $9,291 | $13,937 | $18,583 | $23,228 | $27,874 | $32,520 | $37,165 | $41,811 |
| 6 | $5,543 | $11,086 | $16,630 | $22,173 | $27,716 | $33,259 | $38,803 | $44,346 | $49,889 |
| 7 | $6,431 | $12,861 | $19,292 | $25,722 | $32,153 | $38,583 | $45,014 | $51,445 | $57,875 |
| 8 | $7,308 | $14,616 | $21,923 | $29,231 | $36,539 | $43,847 | $51,155 | $58,462 | $65,770 |
| 9 | $8,175 | $16,350 | $24,525 | $32,700 | $40,875 | $49,050 | $57,225 | $65,400 | $73,575 |
| 10 | $9,032 | $18,065 | $27,097 | $36,129 | $45,162 | $54,194 | $63,226 | $72,259 | $81,291 |
| 11 | $9,880 | $19,760 | $29,640 | $39,519 | $49,399 | $59,279 | $69,159 | $79,039 | $88,919 |
| 12 | $10,718 | $21,435 | $32,153 | $42,871 | $53,589 | $64,306 | $75,024 | $85,742 | $96,460 |
| 13 | $11,546 | $23,092 | $34,638 | $46,184 | $57,730 | $69,276 | $80,822 | $92,368 | $103,914 |
| 14 | $12,365 | $24,730 | $37,095 | $49,460 | $61,825 | $74,189 | $86,554 | $98,919 | $111,284 |
| 15 | $13,174 | $26,349 | $39,523 | $52,698 | $65,872 | $79,047 | $92,221 | $105,395 | $118,570 |
| 16 | $13,975 | $27,949 | $41,924 | $55,899 | $69,874 | $83,848 | $97,823 | $111,798 | $125,773 |
| 17 | $14,766 | $29,532 | $44,298 | $59,064 | $73,829 | $88,595 | $103,361 | $118,127 | $132,893 |
| 18 | $15,548 | $31,096 | $46,644 | $62,192 | $77,740 | $93,288 | $108,836 | $124,384 | $139,932 |
| 19 | $16,321 | $32,642 | $48,964 | $65,285 | $81,606 | $97,927 | $114,249 | $130,570 | $146,891 |
| 20 | $17,086 | $34,171 | $51,257 | $68,343 | $85,428 | $102,514 | $119,599 | $136,685 | $153,771 |
| 21 | $17,841 | $35,683 | $53,524 | $71,365 | $89,207 | $107,048 | $124,889 | $142,731 | $160,572 |
| 22 | $18,588 | $37,177 | $55,765 | $74,354 | $92,942 | $111,530 | $130,119 | $148,707 | $167,295 |
| 23 | $19,327 | $38,654 | $57,981 | $77,308 | $96,635 | $115,961 | $135,288 | $154,615 | $173,942 |
| 24 | $20,057 | $40,114 | $60,171 | $80,228 | $100,285 | $120,342 | $140,399 | $160,456 | $180,513 |
| 25 | $20,779 | $41,558 | $62,336 | $83,115 | $103,894 | $124,673 | $145,452 | $166,230 | $187,009 |
| 26 | $21,492 | $42,985 | $64,477 | $85,969 | $107,462 | $128,954 | $150,446 | $171,939 | $193,431 |
| 27 | $22,198 | $44,396 | $66,593 | $88,791 | $110,989 | $133,187 | $155,384 | $177,582 | $199,780 |
| 28 | $22,895 | $45,790 | $68,685 | $91,581 | $114,476 | $137,371 | $160,266 | $183,161 | $206,056 |
| 29 | $23,585 | $47,169 | $70,754 | $94,338 | $117,923 | $141,507 | $165,092 | $188,676 | $212,261 |
| 30 | $24,266 | $48,532 | $72,798 | $97,064 | $121,330 | $145,597 | $169,863 | $194,129 | $218,395 |

**Annual Expenses**

| Life Expectancies | $1,000 | $2,000 | $3,000 | $4,000 | $5,000 | $6,000 | $7,000 | $8,000 | $9,000 |
|---|---|---|---|---|---|---|---|---|---|
| 31 | $24,940 | $49,880 | $74,820 | $99,759 | $124,699 | $149,639 | $174,579 | $199,519 | $224,459 |
| 32 | $25,606 | $51,212 | $76,818 | $102,424 | $128,030 | $153,636 | $179,242 | $204,848 | $230,453 |
| 33 | $26,264 | $52,529 | $78,793 | $105,058 | $131,322 | $157,587 | $183,851 | $210,115 | $236,380 |
| 34 | $26,915 | $53,831 | $80,746 | $107,662 | $134,577 | $161,492 | $188,408 | $215,323 | $242,239 |
| 35 | $27,559 | $55,118 | $82,677 | $110,236 | $137,795 | $165,354 | $192,913 | $220,472 | $248,031 |
| 36 | $28,195 | $56,390 | $84,585 | $112,781 | $140,976 | $169,171 | $197,366 | $225,561 | $253,756 |
| 37 | $28,824 | $57,648 | $86,472 | $115,296 | $144,121 | $172,945 | $201,769 | $230,593 | $259,417 |
| 38 | $29,446 | $58,892 | $88,338 | $117,784 | $147,229 | $176,675 | $206,121 | $235,567 | $265,013 |
| 39 | $30,061 | $60,121 | $90,182 | $120,242 | $150,303 | $180,363 | $210,424 | $240,485 | $270,545 |
| 40 | $30,668 | $61,337 | $92,005 | $122,673 | $153,341 | $184,010 | $214,678 | $245,346 | $276,014 |
| 41 | $31,269 | $62,538 | $93,807 | $125,076 | $156,345 | $187,614 | $218,883 | $250,152 | $281,421 |
| 42 | $31,863 | $63,726 | $95,589 | $127,452 | $159,314 | $191,177 | $223,040 | $254,903 | $286,766 |
| 43 | $32,450 | $64,900 | $97,350 | $129,800 | $162,250 | $194,700 | $227,150 | $259,600 | $292,050 |
| 44 | $33,030 | $66,061 | $99,091 | $132,122 | $165,152 | $198,183 | $231,213 | $264,243 | $297,274 |
| 45 | $33,604 | $67,208 | $100,813 | $134,417 | $168,021 | $201,625 | $235,230 | $268,834 | $302,438 |
| 46 | $34,171 | $68,343 | $102,514 | $136,686 | $170,857 | $205,029 | $239,200 | $273,372 | $307,543 |
| 47 | $34,732 | $69,465 | $104,197 | $138,929 | $173,661 | $208,394 | $243,126 | $277,858 | $312,590 |
| 48 | $35,287 | $70,573 | $105,860 | $141,147 | $176,433 | $211,720 | $247,006 | $282,293 | $317,580 |
| 49 | $35,835 | $71,669 | $107,504 | $143,339 | $179,173 | $215,008 | $250,843 | $286,678 | $322,512 |
| 50 | $36,377 | $72,753 | $109,130 | $145,506 | $181,883 | $218,259 | $254,636 | $291,012 | $327,389 |
| 51 | $36,912 | $73,824 | $110,736 | $147,649 | $184,561 | $221,473 | $258,385 | $295,297 | $332,209 |
| 52 | $37,442 | $74,883 | $112,325 | $149,767 | $187,208 | $224,650 | $262,092 | $299,533 | $336,975 |
| 53 | $37,965 | $75,930 | $113,895 | $151,861 | $189,826 | $227,791 | $265,756 | $303,721 | $341,686 |
| 54 | $38,483 | $76,965 | $115,448 | $153,931 | $192,413 | $230,896 | $269,379 | $307,861 | $346,344 |
| 55 | $38,994 | $77,988 | $116,983 | $155,977 | $194,971 | $233,965 | $272,960 | $311,954 | $350,948 |
| 56 | $39,500 | $79,000 | $118,500 | $158,000 | $197,500 | $237,000 | $276,500 | $316,000 | $355,500 |
| 57 | $40,000 | $80,000 | $120,000 | $160,000 | $200,000 | $240,000 | $280,000 | $320,000 | $360,000 |
| 58 | $40,494 | $80,989 | $121,483 | $161,977 | $202,472 | $242,966 | $283,460 | $323,955 | $364,449 |
| 59 | $40,983 | $81,966 | $122,949 | $163,932 | $204,915 | $245,898 | $286,881 | $327,864 | $368,847 |
| 60 | $41,466 | $82,932 | $124,398 | $165,864 | $207,330 | $248,796 | $290,262 | $331,728 | $373,195 |

## STARTING PORTFOLIO NEEDED TO FUND VARIOUS ANNUAL EXPENSES
## ASSUMING NO TRUSTEE FEE (CONTINUED)

| Life Expectancies | Annual Expenses $1,000 | $2,000 | $3,000 | $4,000 | $5,000 | $6,000 | $7,000 | $8,000 | $9,000 |
|---|---|---|---|---|---|---|---|---|---|
| 61 | $41,944 | $83,887 | $125,831 | $167,775 | $209,718 | $251,662 | $293,605 | $335,549 | $377,493 |
| 62 | $42,416 | $84,832 | $127,247 | $169,663 | $212,079 | $254,495 | $296,910 | $339,326 | $381,742 |
| 63 | $42,882 | $85,765 | $128,647 | $171,530 | $214,412 | $257,295 | $300,177 | $343,060 | $385,942 |
| 64 | $43,344 | $86,688 | $130,032 | $173,376 | $216,720 | $260,063 | $303,407 | $346,751 | $390,095 |
| 65 | $43,800 | $87,600 | $131,400 | $175,200 | $219,000 | $262,800 | $306,600 | $350,401 | $394,201 |
| 66 | $44,251 | $88,502 | $132,753 | $177,004 | $221,255 | $265,506 | $309,757 | $354,008 | $398,259 |
| 67 | $44,697 | $89,394 | $134,090 | $178,787 | $223,484 | $268,181 | $312,878 | $357,575 | $402,271 |
| 68 | $45,138 | $90,275 | $135,413 | $180,550 | $225,688 | $270,825 | $315,963 | $361,100 | $406,238 |
| 69 | $45,573 | $91,146 | $136,720 | $182,293 | $227,866 | $273,439 | $319,013 | $364,586 | $410,159 |
| 70 | $46,004 | $92,008 | $138,012 | $184,016 | $230,020 | $276,024 | $322,028 | $368,032 | $414,036 |
| 71 | $46,430 | $92,860 | $139,289 | $185,719 | $232,149 | $278,579 | $325,008 | $371,438 | $417,868 |
| 72 | $46,851 | $93,701 | $140,552 | $187,403 | $234,254 | $281,104 | $327,955 | $374,806 | $421,656 |
| 73 | $47,267 | $94,534 | $141,801 | $189,067 | $236,334 | $283,601 | $330,868 | $378,135 | $425,402 |
| 74 | $47,678 | $95,357 | $143,035 | $190,713 | $238,391 | $286,070 | $333,748 | $381,426 | $429,105 |
| 75 | $48,085 | $96,170 | $144,255 | $192,340 | $240,425 | $288,510 | $336,595 | $384,680 | $432,765 |
| 76 | $48,487 | $96,974 | $145,461 | $193,948 | $242,435 | $290,922 | $339,409 | $387,896 | $436,384 |
| 77 | $48,885 | $97,769 | $146,654 | $195,538 | $244,423 | $293,307 | $342,192 | $391,076 | $439,961 |
| 78 | $49,277 | $98,555 | $147,832 | $197,110 | $246,387 | $295,665 | $344,942 | $394,220 | $443,497 |
| 79 | $49,666 | $99,332 | $148,998 | $198,664 | $248,330 | $297,996 | $347,662 | $397,328 | $446,994 |
| 80 | $50,050 | $100,100 | $150,150 | $200,200 | $250,250 | $300,300 | $350,350 | $400,400 | $450,450 |
| 81 | $50,430 | $100,859 | $151,289 | $201,719 | $252,148 | $302,578 | $353,008 | $403,437 | $453,867 |
| 82 | $50,805 | $101,610 | $152,415 | $203,220 | $254,025 | $304,830 | $355,635 | $406,440 | $457,245 |
| 83 | $51,176 | $102,352 | $153,528 | $204,704 | $255,880 | $307,056 | $358,232 | $409,408 | $460,584 |
| 84 | $51,543 | $103,086 | $154,629 | $206,171 | $257,714 | $309,257 | $360,800 | $412,343 | $463,886 |
| 85 | $51,905 | $103,811 | $155,716 | $207,622 | $259,527 | $311,433 | $363,338 | $415,244 | $467,149 |
| 86 | $52,264 | $104,528 | $156,792 | $209,056 | $261,320 | $313,584 | $365,848 | $418,112 | $470,376 |
| 87 | $52,618 | $105,237 | $157,855 | $210,474 | $263,092 | $315,710 | $368,329 | $420,947 | $473,565 |
| 88 | $52,969 | $105,937 | $158,906 | $211,875 | $264,844 | $317,812 | $370,781 | $423,750 | $476,719 |
| 89 | $53,315 | $106,630 | $159,945 | $213,260 | $266,576 | $319,891 | $373,206 | $426,521 | $479,836 |
| 90 | $53,658 | $107,315 | $160,973 | $214,630 | $268,288 | $321,945 | $375,603 | $429,260 | $482,918 |

**Annual Expenses**

| Life Expectancies | $10,000 | $11,000 | $12,000 | $13,000 | $14,000 | $15,000 | $17,500 | $20,000 | $22,500 |
|---|---|---|---|---|---|---|---|---|---|
| 1 | $9,506 | $10,456 | $11,407 | $12,357 | $13,308 | $14,259 | $16,635 | $19,011 | $21,388 |
| 2 | $18,903 | $20,793 | $22,684 | $24,574 | $26,464 | $28,354 | $33,080 | $37,806 | $42,532 |
| 3 | $28,193 | $31,012 | $33,832 | $36,651 | $39,470 | $42,290 | $49,338 | $56,386 | $63,434 |
| 4 | $37,377 | $41,115 | $44,853 | $48,590 | $52,328 | $56,066 | $65,410 | $74,754 | $84,099 |
| 5 | $46,457 | $51,102 | $55,748 | $60,393 | $65,039 | $69,685 | $81,299 | $92,913 | $104,527 |
| 6 | $55,432 | $60,976 | $66,519 | $72,062 | $77,605 | $83,148 | $97,007 | $110,865 | $124,723 |
| 7 | $64,306 | $70,736 | $77,167 | $83,597 | $90,028 | $96,459 | $112,535 | $128,611 | $144,688 |
| 8 | $73,078 | $80,386 | $87,693 | $95,001 | $102,309 | $109,617 | $127,886 | $146,156 | $164,425 |
| 9 | $81,750 | $89,925 | $98,100 | $106,275 | $114,450 | $122,625 | $143,062 | $163,500 | $183,937 |
| 10 | $90,323 | $99,355 | $108,388 | $117,420 | $126,452 | $135,485 | $158,066 | $180,646 | $203,227 |
| 11 | $98,799 | $108,678 | $118,558 | $128,438 | $138,318 | $148,198 | $172,898 | $197,597 | $222,297 |
| 12 | $107,177 | $117,895 | $128,613 | $139,330 | $150,048 | $160,766 | $187,560 | $214,355 | $241,149 |
| 13 | $115,460 | $127,006 | $138,553 | $150,099 | $161,645 | $173,191 | $202,056 | $230,921 | $259,786 |
| 14 | $123,649 | $136,014 | $148,379 | $160,744 | $173,109 | $185,474 | $216,386 | $247,298 | $278,211 |
| 15 | $131,744 | $144,919 | $158,093 | $171,268 | $184,442 | $197,617 | $230,553 | $263,489 | $296,425 |
| 16 | $139,747 | $153,722 | $167,697 | $181,671 | $195,646 | $209,621 | $244,558 | $279,495 | $314,431 |
| 17 | $147,659 | $162,425 | $177,191 | $191,957 | $206,722 | $221,488 | $258,403 | $295,318 | $332,233 |
| 18 | $155,480 | $171,028 | $186,576 | $202,124 | $217,672 | $233,220 | $272,091 | $310,961 | $349,831 |
| 19 | $163,212 | $179,534 | $195,855 | $212,176 | $228,497 | $244,819 | $285,622 | $326,425 | $367,228 |
| 20 | $170,856 | $187,942 | $205,028 | $222,113 | $239,199 | $256,285 | $298,999 | $341,713 | $384,427 |
| 21 | $178,413 | $196,255 | $214,096 | $231,937 | $249,778 | $267,620 | $312,223 | $356,826 | $401,430 |
| 22 | $185,884 | $204,472 | $223,061 | $241,649 | $260,237 | $278,826 | $325,297 | $371,768 | $418,238 |
| 23 | $193,269 | $212,596 | $231,923 | $251,250 | $270,577 | $289,904 | $338,221 | $386,538 | $434,856 |
| 24 | $200,570 | $220,627 | $240,684 | $260,741 | $280,798 | $300,855 | $350,998 | $401,140 | $451,283 |
| 25 | $207,788 | $228,567 | $249,346 | $270,124 | $290,903 | $311,682 | $363,629 | $415,576 | $467,523 |
| 26 | $214,924 | $236,416 | $257,908 | $279,401 | $300,893 | $322,385 | $376,116 | $429,847 | $483,578 |
| 27 | $221,978 | $244,175 | $266,373 | $288,571 | $310,769 | $332,967 | $388,461 | $443,955 | $499,450 |
| 28 | $228,951 | $251,846 | $274,742 | $297,637 | $320,532 | $343,427 | $400,665 | $457,903 | $515,140 |
| 29 | $235,845 | $259,430 | $283,014 | $306,599 | $330,184 | $353,768 | $412,729 | $471,691 | $530,652 |
| 30 | $242,661 | $266,927 | $291,193 | $315,459 | $339,725 | $363,991 | $424,656 | $485,322 | $545,987 |

## CHART FOUR

## STARTING PORTFOLIO NEEDED TO FUND VARIOUS ANNUAL EXPENSES ASSUMING NO TRUSTEE FEE (CONTINUED)

**Annual Expenses**

| Life Expectancies | $10,000 | $11,000 | $12,000 | $13,000 | $14,000 | $15,000 | $17,500 | $20,000 | $22,500 |
|---|---|---|---|---|---|---|---|---|---|
| 31 | $249,399 | $274,338 | $299,278 | $324,218 | $349,158 | $374,098 | $436,447 | $498,797 | $561,147 |
| 32 | $256,059 | $281,665 | $307,271 | $332,877 | $358,483 | $384,089 | $448,104 | $512,119 | $576,134 |
| 33 | $262,644 | $288,909 | $315,173 | $341,438 | $367,702 | $393,966 | $459,628 | $525,289 | $590,950 |
| 34 | $269,154 | $296,069 | $322,985 | $349,900 | $376,816 | $403,731 | $471,020 | $538,308 | $605,597 |
| 35 | $275,590 | $303,149 | $330,707 | $358,266 | $385,825 | $413,384 | $482,282 | $551,179 | $620,076 |
| 36 | $281,952 | $310,147 | $338,342 | $366,537 | $394,732 | $422,927 | $493,415 | $563,903 | $634,391 |
| 37 | $288,241 | $317,065 | $345,889 | $374,714 | $403,538 | $432,362 | $504,422 | $576,482 | $648,543 |
| 38 | $294,459 | $323,905 | $353,351 | $382,797 | $412,243 | $441,688 | $515,303 | $588,918 | $662,533 |
| 39 | $300,606 | $330,666 | $360,727 | $390,788 | $420,848 | $450,909 | $526,060 | $601,212 | $676,363 |
| 40 | $306,683 | $337,351 | $368,019 | $398,687 | $429,356 | $460,024 | $536,694 | $613,365 | $690,036 |
| 41 | $312,690 | $343,959 | $375,228 | $406,497 | $437,766 | $469,035 | $547,207 | $625,380 | $703,552 |
| 42 | $318,629 | $350,492 | $382,355 | $414,218 | $446,080 | $477,943 | $557,601 | $637,258 | $716,915 |
| 43 | $324,500 | $356,950 | $389,400 | $421,850 | $454,300 | $486,750 | $567,875 | $649,000 | $730,125 |
| 44 | $330,304 | $363,335 | $396,365 | $429,395 | $462,426 | $495,456 | $578,032 | $660,608 | $743,184 |
| 45 | $336,042 | $369,646 | $403,251 | $436,855 | $470,459 | $504,063 | $588,074 | $672,084 | $756,095 |
| 46 | $341,715 | $375,886 | $410,058 | $444,229 | $478,401 | $512,572 | $598,001 | $683,429 | $768,858 |
| 47 | $347,323 | $382,055 | $416,787 | $451,519 | $486,252 | $520,984 | $607,814 | $694,645 | $781,476 |
| 48 | $352,866 | $388,153 | $423,440 | $458,726 | $494,013 | $529,300 | $617,516 | $705,733 | $793,949 |
| 49 | $358,347 | $394,182 | $430,016 | $465,851 | $501,686 | $537,520 | $627,107 | $716,694 | $806,281 |
| 50 | $363,765 | $400,142 | $436,518 | $472,895 | $509,271 | $545,648 | $636,589 | $727,530 | $818,471 |
| 51 | $369,121 | $406,034 | $442,946 | $479,858 | $516,770 | $553,682 | $645,962 | $738,243 | $830,523 |
| 52 | $374,417 | $411,858 | $449,300 | $486,742 | $524,183 | $561,625 | $655,229 | $748,833 | $842,437 |
| 53 | $379,651 | $417,616 | $455,582 | $493,547 | $531,512 | $569,477 | $664,390 | $759,303 | $854,216 |
| 54 | $384,826 | $423,309 | $461,792 | $500,274 | $538,757 | $577,240 | $673,446 | $769,653 | $865,859 |
| 55 | $389,942 | $428,937 | $467,931 | $506,925 | $545,919 | $584,914 | $682,399 | $779,885 | $877,371 |
| 56 | $395,000 | $434,500 | $474,000 | $513,500 | $553,000 | $592,500 | $691,250 | $790,000 | $888,750 |
| 57 | $400,000 | $440,000 | $480,000 | $520,000 | $560,000 | $600,000 | $700,000 | $800,000 | $900,000 |
| 58 | $404,943 | $445,437 | $485,932 | $526,426 | $566,920 | $607,415 | $708,650 | $809,886 | $911,122 |
| 59 | $409,830 | $450,813 | $491,796 | $532,779 | $573,762 | $614,745 | $717,202 | $819,659 | $922,117 |
| 60 | $414,661 | $456,127 | $497,593 | $539,059 | $580,525 | $621,991 | $725,656 | $829,321 | $932,986 |

**Annual Expenses**

| Life Expectancies | $10,000 | $11,000 | $12,000 | $13,000 | $14,000 | $15,000 | $17,500 | $20,000 | $22,500 |
|---|---|---|---|---|---|---|---|---|---|
| 61 | $419,436 | $461,380 | $503,324 | $545,267 | $587,211 | $629,154 | $734,014 | $838,873 | $943,732 |
| 62 | $424,158 | $466,573 | $508,989 | $551,405 | $593,821 | $636,236 | $742,276 | $848,315 | $954,354 |
| 63 | $428,825 | $471,707 | $514,590 | $557,472 | $600,355 | $643,237 | $750,444 | $857,650 | $964,856 |
| 64 | $433,439 | $476,783 | $520,127 | $563,471 | $606,815 | $650,159 | $758,518 | $866,878 | $975,238 |
| 65 | $438,001 | $481,801 | $525,601 | $569,401 | $613,201 | $657,001 | $766,501 | $876,001 | $985,501 |
| 66 | $442,510 | $486,761 | $531,012 | $575,263 | $619,514 | $663,765 | $774,393 | $885,020 | $995,648 |
| 67 | $446,968 | $491,665 | $536,362 | $581,059 | $625,755 | $670,452 | $782,194 | $893,936 | $1,005,678 |
| 68 | $451,375 | $496,513 | $541,650 | $586,788 | $631,926 | $677,063 | $789,907 | $902,751 | $1,015,595 |
| 69 | $455,732 | $501,306 | $546,879 | $592,452 | $638,025 | $683,599 | $797,532 | $911,465 | $1,025,398 |
| 70 | $460,040 | $506,044 | $552,048 | $598,051 | $644,055 | $690,059 | $805,069 | $920,079 | $1,035,089 |
| 71 | $464,298 | $510,727 | $557,157 | $603,587 | $650,017 | $696,447 | $812,521 | $928,595 | $1,044,670 |
| 72 | $468,507 | $515,358 | $562,209 | $609,059 | $655,910 | $702,761 | $819,888 | $937,014 | $1,054,141 |
| 73 | $472,669 | $519,936 | $567,202 | $614,469 | $661,736 | $709,003 | $827,170 | $945,337 | $1,063,505 |
| 74 | $476,783 | $524,461 | $572,139 | $619,818 | $667,496 | $715,174 | $834,370 | $953,566 | $1,072,761 |
| 75 | $480,850 | $528,935 | $577,020 | $625,105 | $673,190 | $721,275 | $841,487 | $961,700 | $1,081,912 |
| 76 | $484,871 | $533,358 | $581,845 | $630,332 | $678,819 | $727,306 | $848,524 | $969,741 | $1,090,959 |
| 77 | $488,845 | $537,730 | $586,615 | $635,499 | $684,384 | $733,268 | $855,480 | $977,691 | $1,099,902 |
| 78 | $492,775 | $542,052 | $591,330 | $640,607 | $689,885 | $739,162 | $862,356 | $985,550 | $1,108,744 |
| 79 | $496,660 | $546,326 | $595,992 | $645,658 | $695,324 | $744,990 | $869,154 | $993,319 | $1,117,484 |
| 80 | $500,500 | $550,550 | $600,600 | $650,650 | $700,700 | $750,750 | $875,875 | $1,001,000 | $1,126,125 |
| 81 | $504,297 | $554,726 | $605,156 | $655,586 | $706,015 | $756,445 | $882,519 | $1,008,593 | $1,134,667 |
| 82 | $508,050 | $558,855 | $609,660 | $660,465 | $711,270 | $762,075 | $889,087 | $1,016,100 | $1,143,112 |
| 83 | $511,760 | $562,936 | $614,112 | $665,288 | $716,465 | $767,641 | $895,581 | $1,023,521 | $1,151,461 |
| 84 | $515,429 | $566,971 | $618,514 | $670,057 | $721,600 | $773,143 | $902,000 | $1,030,857 | $1,159,714 |
| 85 | $519,055 | $570,960 | $622,866 | $674,771 | $726,677 | $778,582 | $908,346 | $1,038,110 | $1,167,873 |
| 86 | $522,640 | $574,904 | $627,168 | $679,432 | $731,696 | $783,960 | $914,620 | $1,045,279 | $1,175,939 |
| 87 | $526,184 | $578,802 | $631,421 | $684,039 | $736,657 | $789,276 | $920,822 | $1,052,368 | $1,183,913 |
| 88 | $529,687 | $582,656 | $635,625 | $688,594 | $741,562 | $794,531 | $926,953 | $1,059,375 | $1,191,797 |
| 89 | $533,151 | $586,466 | $639,781 | $693,096 | $746,411 | $799,727 | $933,014 | $1,066,302 | $1,199,590 |
| 90 | $536,575 | $590,233 | $643,890 | $697,548 | $751,205 | $804,863 | $939,007 | $1,073,150 | $1,207,294 |

## STARTING PORTFOLIO NEEDED TO FUND VARIOUS ANNUAL EXPENSES ASSUMING NO TRUSTEE FEE (CONTINUED)

| Life Expectancies | Annual Expenses $25,000 | $27,500 | $30,000 | $35,000 | $40,000 | $45,000 | $50,000 |
|---|---|---|---|---|---|---|---|
| 1 | $23,764 | $26,141 | $28,517 | $33,270 | $38,023 | $42,776 | $47,529 |
| 2 | $47,257 | $51,983 | $56,709 | $66,160 | $75,612 | $85,063 | $94,515 |
| 3 | $70,483 | $77,531 | $84,579 | $98,676 | $112,772 | $126,869 | $140,965 |
| 4 | $93,443 | $102,787 | $112,131 | $130,820 | $149,509 | $168,197 | $186,886 |
| 5 | $116,141 | $127,755 | $139,370 | $162,598 | $185,826 | $209,054 | $232,283 |
| 6 | $138,581 | $152,439 | $166,297 | $194,013 | $221,729 | $249,445 | $277,161 |
| 7 | $160,764 | $176,841 | $192,917 | $225,070 | $257,223 | $289,376 | $321,528 |
| 8 | $182,695 | $200,964 | $219,234 | $255,773 | $292,311 | $328,850 | $365,389 |
| 9 | $204,375 | $224,812 | $245,250 | $286,125 | $327,000 | $367,875 | $408,750 |
| 10 | $225,808 | $248,389 | $270,970 | $316,131 | $361,293 | $406,454 | $451,616 |
| 11 | $246,996 | $271,696 | $296,396 | $345,795 | $395,194 | $444,594 | $493,993 |
| 12 | $267,943 | $294,738 | $321,532 | $375,121 | $428,709 | $482,298 | $535,887 |
| 13 | $288,651 | $317,516 | $346,381 | $404,112 | $461,842 | $519,572 | $577,302 |
| 14 | $309,123 | $340,035 | $370,947 | $432,772 | $494,596 | $556,421 | $618,246 |
| 15 | $329,361 | $362,297 | $395,233 | $461,105 | $526,977 | $592,850 | $658,722 |
| 16 | $349,368 | $384,305 | $419,242 | $489,116 | $558,989 | $628,863 | $698,736 |
| 17 | $369,147 | $406,062 | $442,977 | $516,806 | $590,636 | $664,465 | $738,295 |
| 18 | $388,701 | $427,571 | $466,441 | $544,181 | $621,921 | $699,661 | $777,401 |
| 19 | $408,031 | $448,834 | $489,637 | $571,244 | $652,850 | $734,456 | $816,062 |
| 20 | $427,141 | $469,855 | $512,569 | $597,997 | $683,426 | $768,854 | $854,282 |
| 21 | $446,033 | $490,636 | $535,240 | $624,446 | $713,653 | $802,859 | $892,066 |
| 22 | $464,709 | $511,180 | $557,651 | $650,593 | $743,535 | $836,477 | $929,419 |
| 23 | $483,173 | $531,490 | $579,807 | $676,442 | $773,077 | $869,711 | $966,346 |
| 24 | $501,426 | $551,568 | $601,711 | $701,996 | $802,281 | $902,566 | $1,002,851 |
| 25 | $519,470 | $571,417 | $623,364 | $727,258 | $831,152 | $935,046 | $1,038,940 |
| 26 | $537,309 | $591,040 | $644,771 | $752,232 | $859,694 | $967,156 | $1,074,618 |
| 27 | $554,944 | $610,439 | $665,933 | $776,922 | $887,911 | $998,900 | $1,109,888 |
| 28 | $572,378 | $629,616 | $686,854 | $801,330 | $915,805 | $1,030,281 | $1,144,757 |
| 29 | $589,613 | $648,575 | $707,536 | $825,459 | $943,382 | $1,061,304 | $1,179,227 |
| 30 | $606,652 | $667,317 | $727,983 | $849,313 | $970,643 | $1,091,974 | $1,213,304 |

**Annual Expenses**

| Life Expectancies | $25,000 | $27,500 | $30,000 | $35,000 | $40,000 | $45,000 | $50,000 |
|---|---|---|---|---|---|---|---|
| 31 | $623,496 | $685,846 | $748,196 | $872,895 | $997,594 | $1,122,294 | $1,246,993 |
| 32 | $640,149 | $704,163 | $768,178 | $896,208 | $1,024,238 | $1,152,267 | $1,280,297 |
| 33 | $656,611 | $722,272 | $787,933 | $919,255 | $1,050,577 | $1,181,899 | $1,313,221 |
| 34 | $672,885 | $740,174 | $807,462 | $942,039 | $1,076,616 | $1,211,193 | $1,345,770 |
| 35 | $688,974 | $757,871 | $826,769 | $964,563 | $1,102,358 | $1,240,153 | $1,377,948 |
| 36 | $704,879 | $775,367 | $845,855 | $986,831 | $1,127,807 | $1,268,782 | $1,409,758 |
| 37 | $720,603 | $792,663 | $864,724 | $1,008,844 | $1,152,965 | $1,297,085 | $1,441,206 |
| 38 | $736,147 | $809,762 | $883,377 | $1,030,606 | $1,177,836 | $1,325,065 | $1,472,295 |
| 39 | $751,515 | $826,666 | $901,817 | $1,052,120 | $1,202,423 | $1,352,726 | $1,503,029 |
| 40 | $766,706 | $843,377 | $920,048 | $1,073,389 | $1,226,730 | $1,380,071 | $1,533,413 |
| 41 | $781,725 | $859,897 | $938,070 | $1,094,415 | $1,250,760 | $1,407,105 | $1,563,450 |
| 42 | $796,572 | $876,229 | $955,887 | $1,115,201 | $1,274,515 | $1,433,830 | $1,593,144 |
| 43 | $811,250 | $892,375 | $973,500 | $1,135,750 | $1,298,000 | $1,460,250 | $1,622,500 |
| 44 | $825,761 | $908,337 | $990,913 | $1,156,065 | $1,321,217 | $1,486,369 | $1,651,521 |
| 45 | $840,105 | $924,116 | $1,008,127 | $1,176,148 | $1,344,169 | $1,512,190 | $1,680,211 |
| 46 | $854,287 | $939,715 | $1,025,144 | $1,196,001 | $1,366,859 | $1,537,716 | $1,708,574 |
| 47 | $868,306 | $955,137 | $1,041,968 | $1,215,629 | $1,389,290 | $1,562,951 | $1,736,613 |
| 48 | $882,166 | $970,383 | $1,058,599 | $1,235,032 | $1,411,465 | $1,587,899 | $1,764,332 |
| 49 | $895,867 | $985,454 | $1,075,041 | $1,254,214 | $1,433,388 | $1,612,561 | $1,791,735 |
| 50 | $909,413 | $1,000,354 | $1,091,295 | $1,273,178 | $1,455,060 | $1,636,943 | $1,818,825 |
| 51 | $922,803 | $1,015,084 | $1,107,364 | $1,291,925 | $1,476,485 | $1,661,046 | $1,845,607 |
| 52 | $936,041 | $1,029,646 | $1,123,250 | $1,310,458 | $1,497,666 | $1,684,875 | $1,872,083 |
| 53 | $949,128 | $1,044,041 | $1,138,954 | $1,328,780 | $1,518,605 | $1,708,431 | $1,898,257 |
| 54 | $962,066 | $1,058,273 | $1,154,479 | $1,346,893 | $1,539,306 | $1,731,719 | $1,924,132 |
| 55 | $974,856 | $1,072,342 | $1,169,827 | $1,364,799 | $1,559,770 | $1,754,741 | $1,949,712 |
| 56 | $987,500 | $1,086,250 | $1,185,001 | $1,382,501 | $1,580,001 | $1,777,501 | $1,975,001 |
| 57 | $1,000,000 | $1,100,000 | $1,200,001 | $1,400,001 | $1,600,001 | $1,800,001 | $2,000,001 |
| 58 | $1,012,358 | $1,113,594 | $1,214,829 | $1,417,301 | $1,619,773 | $1,822,244 | $2,024,716 |
| 59 | $1,024,574 | $1,127,032 | $1,229,489 | $1,434,404 | $1,639,319 | $1,844,234 | $2,049,149 |
| 60 | $1,036,651 | $1,140,317 | $1,243,982 | $1,451,312 | $1,658,642 | $1,865,973 | $2,073,303 |

# STARTING PORTFOLIO NEEDED TO FUND VARIOUS ANNUAL EXPENSES
## ASSUMING NO TRUSTEE FEE (CONTINUED)

| Life Expectancies | Annual Expenses $25,000 | $27,500 | $30,000 | $35,000 | $40,000 | $45,000 | $50,000 |
|---|---|---|---|---|---|---|---|
| 61 | $1,048,591 | $1,153,450 | $1,258,309 | $1,468,027 | $1,677,745 | $1,887,463 | $2,097,181 |
| 62 | $1,060,394 | $1,166,433 | $1,272,473 | $1,484,551 | $1,696,630 | $1,908,709 | $2,120,788 |
| 63 | $1,072,062 | $1,179,269 | $1,286,475 | $1,500,887 | $1,715,300 | $1,929,712 | $2,144,125 |
| 64 | $1,083,598 | $1,191,958 | $1,300,317 | $1,517,037 | $1,733,756 | $1,950,476 | $2,167,196 |
| 65 | $1,095,002 | $1,204,502 | $1,314,002 | $1,533,002 | $1,752,003 | $1,971,003 | $2,190,003 |
| 66 | $1,106,275 | $1,216,903 | $1,327,530 | $1,548,786 | $1,770,041 | $1,991,296 | $2,212,551 |
| 67 | $1,117,421 | $1,229,163 | $1,340,905 | $1,564,389 | $1,787,873 | $2,011,357 | $2,234,841 |
| 68 | $1,128,439 | $1,241,282 | $1,354,126 | $1,579,814 | $1,805,502 | $2,031,189 | $2,256,877 |
| 69 | $1,139,331 | $1,253,264 | $1,367,197 | $1,595,063 | $1,822,929 | $2,050,796 | $2,278,662 |
| 70 | $1,150,099 | $1,265,109 | $1,380,119 | $1,610,139 | $1,840,158 | $2,070,178 | $2,300,198 |
| 71 | $1,160,744 | $1,276,819 | $1,392,893 | $1,625,042 | $1,857,191 | $2,089,340 | $2,321,488 |
| 72 | $1,171,268 | $1,288,395 | $1,405,522 | $1,639,775 | $1,874,029 | $2,108,282 | $2,342,536 |
| 73 | $1,181,672 | $1,299,839 | $1,418,006 | $1,654,341 | $1,890,675 | $2,127,009 | $2,363,344 |
| 74 | $1,191,957 | $1,311,153 | $1,430,348 | $1,668,740 | $1,907,131 | $2,145,523 | $2,383,914 |
| 75 | $1,202,125 | $1,322,337 | $1,442,550 | $1,682,975 | $1,923,400 | $2,163,825 | $2,404,249 |
| 76 | $1,212,177 | $1,333,394 | $1,454,612 | $1,697,047 | $1,939,482 | $2,181,918 | $2,424,353 |
| 77 | $1,222,114 | $1,344,325 | $1,466,536 | $1,710,959 | $1,955,382 | $2,199,805 | $2,444,227 |
| 78 | $1,231,937 | $1,355,131 | $1,478,325 | $1,724,712 | $1,971,100 | $2,217,487 | $2,463,875 |
| 79 | $1,241,649 | $1,365,814 | $1,489,979 | $1,738,309 | $1,986,639 | $2,234,969 | $2,483,298 |
| 80 | $1,251,250 | $1,376,375 | $1,501,500 | $1,751,750 | $2,002,000 | $2,252,250 | $2,502,500 |
| 81 | $1,260,742 | $1,386,816 | $1,512,890 | $1,765,038 | $2,017,187 | $2,269,335 | $2,521,483 |
| 82 | $1,270,125 | $1,397,137 | $1,524,150 | $1,778,175 | $2,032,200 | $2,286,225 | $2,540,250 |
| 83 | $1,279,401 | $1,407,341 | $1,535,281 | $1,791,161 | $2,047,042 | $2,302,922 | $2,558,802 |
| 84 | $1,288,571 | $1,417,428 | $1,546,286 | $1,804,000 | $2,061,714 | $2,319,428 | $2,577,143 |
| 85 | $1,297,637 | $1,427,401 | $1,557,164 | $1,816,692 | $2,076,219 | $2,335,747 | $2,595,274 |
| 86 | $1,306,599 | $1,437,259 | $1,567,919 | $1,829,239 | $2,090,559 | $2,351,879 | $2,613,199 |
| 87 | $1,315,459 | $1,447,005 | $1,578,551 | $1,841,643 | $2,104,735 | $2,367,827 | $2,630,919 |
| 88 | $1,324,218 | $1,456,640 | $1,589,062 | $1,853,906 | $2,118,749 | $2,383,593 | $2,648,437 |
| 89 | $1,332,878 | $1,466,165 | $1,599,453 | $1,866,029 | $2,132,604 | $2,399,180 | $2,665,755 |
| 90 | $1,341,438 | $1,475,582 | $1,609,725 | $1,878,013 | $2,146,301 | $2,414,588 | $2,682,876 |

## Chart Five

## Starting Portfolio Needed to Fund Various Annual Expenses
### Assuming a 1% Trustee Fee

| Life Expectancies | Annual Expenses $1,000 | $2,000 | $3,000 | $4,000 | $5,000 | $6,000 | $7,000 | $8,000 | $9,000 |
|---|---|---|---|---|---|---|---|---|---|
| 1 | $960 | $1,919 | $2,879 | $3,839 | $4,798 | $5,758 | $6,718 | $7,678 | $8,637 |
| 2 | $1,918 | $3,835 | $5,753 | $7,670 | $9,588 | $11,505 | $13,423 | $15,340 | $17,258 |
| 3 | $2,874 | $5,747 | $8,621 | $11,494 | $14,368 | $17,241 | $20,115 | $22,988 | $25,862 |
| 4 | $3,828 | $7,655 | $11,483 | $15,311 | $19,139 | $22,966 | $26,794 | $30,622 | $34,450 |
| 5 | $4,780 | $9,560 | $14,340 | $19,120 | $23,900 | $28,680 | $33,461 | $38,241 | $43,021 |
| 6 | $5,731 | $11,461 | $17,192 | $22,922 | $28,653 | $34,384 | $40,114 | $45,845 | $51,575 |
| 7 | $6,679 | $13,359 | $20,038 | $26,717 | $33,396 | $40,076 | $46,755 | $53,434 | $60,114 |
| 8 | $7,626 | $15,252 | $22,878 | $30,505 | $38,131 | $45,757 | $53,383 | $61,009 | $68,635 |
| 9 | $8,571 | $17,142 | $25,714 | $34,285 | $42,856 | $51,427 | $59,999 | $68,570 | $77,141 |
| 10 | $9,514 | $19,029 | $28,543 | $38,058 | $47,572 | $57,087 | $66,601 | $76,116 | $85,630 |
| 11 | $10,456 | $20,912 | $31,368 | $41,824 | $52,279 | $62,735 | $73,191 | $83,647 | $94,103 |
| 12 | $11,396 | $22,791 | $34,187 | $45,582 | $56,978 | $68,373 | $79,769 | $91,164 | $102,560 |
| 13 | $12,333 | $24,667 | $37,000 | $49,333 | $61,667 | $74,000 | $86,333 | $98,667 | $111,000 |
| 14 | $13,269 | $26,539 | $39,808 | $53,077 | $66,347 | $79,616 | $92,885 | $106,155 | $119,424 |
| 15 | $14,204 | $28,407 | $42,611 | $56,814 | $71,018 | $85,221 | $99,425 | $113,629 | $127,832 |
| 16 | $15,136 | $30,272 | $45,408 | $60,544 | $75,680 | $90,816 | $105,952 | $121,088 | $136,224 |
| 17 | $16,067 | $32,133 | $48,200 | $64,267 | $80,333 | $96,400 | $112,467 | $128,533 | $144,600 |
| 18 | $16,996 | $33,991 | $50,987 | $67,982 | $84,978 | $101,973 | $118,969 | $135,964 | $152,960 |
| 19 | $17,923 | $35,845 | $53,768 | $71,690 | $89,613 | $107,535 | $125,458 | $143,381 | $161,303 |
| 20 | $18,848 | $37,696 | $56,544 | $75,391 | $94,239 | $113,087 | $131,935 | $150,783 | $169,631 |
| 21 | $19,771 | $39,543 | $59,314 | $79,086 | $98,857 | $118,628 | $138,400 | $158,171 | $177,942 |
| 22 | $20,693 | $41,386 | $62,079 | $82,773 | $103,466 | $124,159 | $144,852 | $165,545 | $186,238 |
| 23 | $21,613 | $43,226 | $64,839 | $86,452 | $108,066 | $129,679 | $151,292 | $172,905 | $194,518 |
| 24 | $22,531 | $45,063 | $67,594 | $90,125 | $112,657 | $135,188 | $157,719 | $180,251 | $202,782 |
| 25 | $23,448 | $46,896 | $70,343 | $93,791 | $117,239 | $140,687 | $164,134 | $187,582 | $211,030 |
| 26 | $24,362 | $48,725 | $73,087 | $97,450 | $121,812 | $146,175 | $170,537 | $194,900 | $219,262 |
| 27 | $25,275 | $50,551 | $75,826 | $101,102 | $126,377 | $151,652 | $176,928 | $202,203 | $227,478 |
| 28 | $26,187 | $52,373 | $78,560 | $104,746 | $130,933 | $157,119 | $183,306 | $209,492 | $235,679 |
| 29 | $27,096 | $54,192 | $81,288 | $108,384 | $135,480 | $162,576 | $189,672 | $216,768 | $243,864 |
| 30 | $28,004 | $56,007 | $84,011 | $112,015 | $140,018 | $168,022 | $196,026 | $224,029 | $252,033 |

## STARTING PORTFOLIO NEEDED TO FUND VARIOUS ANNUAL EXPENSES
### ASSUMING A 1% TRUSTEE FEE (CONTINUED)

| Life Expectancies | Annual Expenses $1,000 | $2,000 | $3,000 | $4,000 | $5,000 | $6,000 | $7,000 | $8,000 | $9,000 |
|---|---|---|---|---|---|---|---|---|---|
| 31 | $28,910 | $57,819 | $86,729 | $115,638 | $144,548 | $173,458 | $202,367 | $231,277 | $260,187 |
| 32 | $29,814 | $59,628 | $89,441 | $119,255 | $149,069 | $178,883 | $208,697 | $238,511 | $268,324 |
| 33 | $30,716 | $61,433 | $92,149 | $122,865 | $153,581 | $184,298 | $215,014 | $245,730 | $276,447 |
| 34 | $31,617 | $63,234 | $94,851 | $126,468 | $158,085 | $189,702 | $221,319 | $252,936 | $284,553 |
| 35 | $32,516 | $65,032 | $97,548 | $130,064 | $162,580 | $195,096 | $227,612 | $260,128 | $292,644 |
| 36 | $33,413 | $66,827 | $100,240 | $133,653 | $167,067 | $200,480 | $233,893 | $267,307 | $300,720 |
| 37 | $34,309 | $68,618 | $102,927 | $137,236 | $171,544 | $205,853 | $240,162 | $274,471 | $308,780 |
| 38 | $35,203 | $70,405 | $105,608 | $140,811 | $176,014 | $211,216 | $246,419 | $281,622 | $316,824 |
| 39 | $36,095 | $72,190 | $108,285 | $144,379 | $180,474 | $216,569 | $252,664 | $288,759 | $324,854 |
| 40 | $36,985 | $73,971 | $110,956 | $147,941 | $184,926 | $221,912 | $258,897 | $295,882 | $332,867 |
| 41 | $37,874 | $75,748 | $113,622 | $151,496 | $189,370 | $227,244 | $265,118 | $302,992 | $340,866 |
| 42 | $38,761 | $77,522 | $116,283 | $155,044 | $193,805 | $232,566 | $271,327 | $310,088 | $348,849 |
| 43 | $39,646 | $79,293 | $118,939 | $158,585 | $198,231 | $237,878 | $277,524 | $317,170 | $356,816 |
| 44 | $40,530 | $81,060 | $121,590 | $162,119 | $202,649 | $243,179 | $283,709 | $324,239 | $364,769 |
| 45 | $41,412 | $82,824 | $124,235 | $165,647 | $207,059 | $248,471 | $289,882 | $331,294 | $372,706 |
| 46 | $42,292 | $84,584 | $126,876 | $169,168 | $211,460 | $253,752 | $296,044 | $338,336 | $380,628 |
| 47 | $43,170 | $86,341 | $129,511 | $172,682 | $215,852 | $259,023 | $302,193 | $345,364 | $388,534 |
| 48 | $44,047 | $88,095 | $132,142 | $176,189 | $220,237 | $264,284 | $308,331 | $352,378 | $396,426 |
| 49 | $44,922 | $89,845 | $134,767 | $179,690 | $224,612 | $269,535 | $314,457 | $359,380 | $404,302 |
| 50 | $45,796 | $91,592 | $137,388 | $183,184 | $228,980 | $274,776 | $320,572 | $366,367 | $412,163 |
| 51 | $46,668 | $93,335 | $140,003 | $186,671 | $233,339 | $280,006 | $326,674 | $373,342 | $420,010 |
| 52 | $47,538 | $95,076 | $142,614 | $190,151 | $237,689 | $285,227 | $332,765 | $380,303 | $427,841 |
| 53 | $48,406 | $96,813 | $145,219 | $193,625 | $242,031 | $290,438 | $338,844 | $387,250 | $435,657 |
| 54 | $49,273 | $98,546 | $147,819 | $197,092 | $246,365 | $295,638 | $344,912 | $394,185 | $443,458 |
| 55 | $50,138 | $100,276 | $150,415 | $200,553 | $250,691 | $300,829 | $350,967 | $401,106 | $451,244 |
| 56 | $51,002 | $102,003 | $153,005 | $204,007 | $255,008 | $306,010 | $357,012 | $408,013 | $459,015 |
| 57 | $51,863 | $103,727 | $155,590 | $207,454 | $259,317 | $311,181 | $363,044 | $414,908 | $466,771 |
| 58 | $52,724 | $105,447 | $158,171 | $210,894 | $263,618 | $316,342 | $369,065 | $421,789 | $474,512 |
| 59 | $53,582 | $107,164 | $160,746 | $214,328 | $267,910 | $321,493 | $375,075 | $428,657 | $482,239 |
| 60 | $54,439 | $108,878 | $163,317 | $217,756 | $272,195 | $326,634 | $381,073 | $435,512 | $489,950 |

**Annual Expenses**

| Life Expectancies | $1,000 | $2,000 | $3,000 | $4,000 | $5,000 | $6,000 | $7,000 | $8,000 | $9,000 |
|---|---|---|---|---|---|---|---|---|---|
| 61 | $55,294 | $110,588 | $165,882 | $221,177 | $276,471 | $331,765 | $387,059 | $442,353 | $497,647 |
| 62 | $56,148 | $112,295 | $168,443 | $224,591 | $280,739 | $336,886 | $393,034 | $449,182 | $505,329 |
| 63 | $57,000 | $113,999 | $170,999 | $227,999 | $284,998 | $341,998 | $398,997 | $455,997 | $512,997 |
| 64 | $57,850 | $115,700 | $173,550 | $231,400 | $289,250 | $347,100 | $404,949 | $462,799 | $520,649 |
| 65 | $58,699 | $117,397 | $176,096 | $234,794 | $293,493 | $352,191 | $410,890 | $469,589 | $528,287 |
| 66 | $59,546 | $119,091 | $178,637 | $238,182 | $297,728 | $357,274 | $416,819 | $476,365 | $535,910 |
| 67 | $60,391 | $120,782 | $181,173 | $241,564 | $301,955 | $362,346 | $422,737 | $483,128 | $543,519 |
| 68 | $61,235 | $122,470 | $183,704 | $244,939 | $306,174 | $367,409 | $428,644 | $489,878 | $551,113 |
| 69 | $62,077 | $124,154 | $186,231 | $248,308 | $310,385 | $372,462 | $434,539 | $496,616 | $558,693 |
| 70 | $62,917 | $125,835 | $188,752 | $251,670 | $314,587 | $377,505 | $440,422 | $503,340 | $566,257 |
| 71 | $63,756 | $127,513 | $191,269 | $255,026 | $318,782 | $382,539 | $446,295 | $510,051 | $573,808 |
| 72 | $64,594 | $129,187 | $193,781 | $258,375 | $322,969 | $387,562 | $452,156 | $516,750 | $581,344 |
| 73 | $65,429 | $130,859 | $196,288 | $261,718 | $327,147 | $392,577 | $458,006 | $523,436 | $588,865 |
| 74 | $66,264 | $132,527 | $198,791 | $265,054 | $331,318 | $397,581 | $463,845 | $530,108 | $596,372 |
| 75 | $67,096 | $134,192 | $201,288 | $268,384 | $335,480 | $402,576 | $469,672 | $536,769 | $603,865 |
| 76 | $67,927 | $135,854 | $203,781 | $271,708 | $339,635 | $407,562 | $475,489 | $543,416 | $611,343 |
| 77 | $68,756 | $137,513 | $206,269 | $275,025 | $343,781 | $412,538 | $481,294 | $550,050 | $618,807 |
| 78 | $69,584 | $139,168 | $208,752 | $278,336 | $347,920 | $417,504 | $487,088 | $556,672 | $626,256 |
| 79 | $70,410 | $140,820 | $211,230 | $281,641 | $352,051 | $422,461 | $492,871 | $563,281 | $633,691 |
| 80 | $71,235 | $142,469 | $213,704 | $284,939 | $356,173 | $427,408 | $498,643 | $569,878 | $641,112 |
| 81 | $72,058 | $144,115 | $216,173 | $288,231 | $360,288 | $432,346 | $504,404 | $576,461 | $648,519 |
| 82 | $72,879 | $145,758 | $218,637 | $291,516 | $364,395 | $437,274 | $510,153 | $583,032 | $655,911 |
| 83 | $73,699 | $147,398 | $221,097 | $294,795 | $368,494 | $442,193 | $515,892 | $589,591 | $663,290 |
| 84 | $74,517 | $149,034 | $223,551 | $298,068 | $372,585 | $447,103 | $521,620 | $596,137 | $670,654 |
| 85 | $75,334 | $150,668 | $226,001 | $301,335 | $376,669 | $452,003 | $527,336 | $602,670 | $678,004 |
| 86 | $76,149 | $152,298 | $228,447 | $304,595 | $380,744 | $456,893 | $533,042 | $609,191 | $685,340 |
| 87 | $76,962 | $153,925 | $230,887 | $307,850 | $384,812 | $461,774 | $538,737 | $615,699 | $692,662 |
| 88 | $77,774 | $155,549 | $233,323 | $311,097 | $388,872 | $466,646 | $544,421 | $622,195 | $699,969 |
| 89 | $78,585 | $157,170 | $235,754 | $314,339 | $392,924 | $471,509 | $550,093 | $628,678 | $707,263 |
| 90 | $79,394 | $158,787 | $238,181 | $317,575 | $396,968 | $476,362 | $555,755 | $635,149 | $714,543 |

## STARTING PORTFOLIO NEEDED TO FUND VARIOUS ANNUAL EXPENSES
### ASSUMING A 1% TRUSTEE FEE (CONTINUED)

| Life Expectancies | Annual Expenses $10,000 | $11,000 | $12,000 | $13,000 | $14,000 | $15,000 | $17,500 | $20,000 | $22,500 |
|---|---|---|---|---|---|---|---|---|---|
| 1 | $9,597 | $10,557 | $11,516 | $12,476 | $13,436 | $14,395 | $16,795 | $19,194 | $21,593 |
| 2 | $19,175 | $21,093 | $23,011 | $24,928 | $26,846 | $28,763 | $33,557 | $38,351 | $43,145 |
| 3 | $28,736 | $31,609 | $34,483 | $37,356 | $40,230 | $43,103 | $50,287 | $57,471 | $64,655 |
| 4 | $38,277 | $42,105 | $45,933 | $49,761 | $53,588 | $57,416 | $66,985 | $76,555 | $86,124 |
| 5 | $47,801 | $52,581 | $57,361 | $62,141 | $66,921 | $71,701 | $83,651 | $95,602 | $107,552 |
| 6 | $57,306 | $63,037 | $68,767 | $74,498 | $80,228 | $85,959 | $100,285 | $114,612 | $128,938 |
| 7 | $66,793 | $73,472 | $80,151 | $86,831 | $93,510 | $100,189 | $116,888 | $133,586 | $150,284 |
| 8 | $76,262 | $83,888 | $91,514 | $99,140 | $106,766 | $114,392 | $133,458 | $152,523 | $171,589 |
| 9 | $85,712 | $94,283 | $102,855 | $111,426 | $119,997 | $128,568 | $149,996 | $171,424 | $192,852 |
| 10 | $95,145 | $104,659 | $114,174 | $123,688 | $133,202 | $142,717 | $166,503 | $190,289 | $214,075 |
| 11 | $104,559 | $115,015 | $125,471 | $135,927 | $146,382 | $156,838 | $182,978 | $209,118 | $235,258 |
| 12 | $113,955 | $125,351 | $136,746 | $148,142 | $159,537 | $170,933 | $199,422 | $227,910 | $256,399 |
| 13 | $123,333 | $135,667 | $148,000 | $160,333 | $172,667 | $185,000 | $215,833 | $246,667 | $277,500 |
| 14 | $132,694 | $145,963 | $159,232 | $172,502 | $185,771 | $199,040 | $232,214 | $265,387 | $298,561 |
| 15 | $142,036 | $156,239 | $170,443 | $184,647 | $198,850 | $213,054 | $248,563 | $284,072 | $319,581 |
| 16 | $151,360 | $166,496 | $181,632 | $196,768 | $211,904 | $227,040 | $264,880 | $302,720 | $340,560 |
| 17 | $160,667 | $176,733 | $192,800 | $208,866 | $224,933 | $241,000 | $281,166 | $321,333 | $361,500 |
| 18 | $169,955 | $186,951 | $203,946 | $220,942 | $237,937 | $254,933 | $297,421 | $339,910 | $382,399 |
| 19 | $179,226 | $197,148 | $215,071 | $232,994 | $250,916 | $268,839 | $313,645 | $358,452 | $403,258 |
| 20 | $188,479 | $207,327 | $226,174 | $245,022 | $263,870 | $282,718 | $329,838 | $376,957 | $424,077 |
| 21 | $197,714 | $217,485 | $237,257 | $257,028 | $276,799 | $296,571 | $345,999 | $395,428 | $444,856 |
| 22 | $206,931 | $227,624 | $248,318 | $269,011 | $289,704 | $310,397 | $362,130 | $413,863 | $465,595 |
| 23 | $216,131 | $237,744 | $259,357 | $280,970 | $302,584 | $324,197 | $378,229 | $432,262 | $486,295 |
| 24 | $225,313 | $247,844 | $270,376 | $292,907 | $315,438 | $337,970 | $394,298 | $450,626 | $506,955 |
| 25 | $234,478 | $257,925 | $281,373 | $304,821 | $328,269 | $351,716 | $410,336 | $468,955 | $527,575 |
| 26 | $243,625 | $267,987 | $292,349 | $316,712 | $341,074 | $365,437 | $426,343 | $487,249 | $548,155 |
| 27 | $252,754 | $278,029 | $303,305 | $328,580 | $353,855 | $379,131 | $442,319 | $505,508 | $568,696 |
| 28 | $261,866 | $288,052 | $314,239 | $340,425 | $366,612 | $392,798 | $458,265 | $523,731 | $589,198 |
| 29 | $270,960 | $298,056 | $325,152 | $352,248 | $379,344 | $406,440 | $474,180 | $541,920 | $609,660 |
| 30 | $280,037 | $308,040 | $336,044 | $364,048 | $392,051 | $420,055 | $490,064 | $560,074 | $630,083 |

**Annual Expenses**

| Life Expectancies | $10,000 | $11,000 | $12,000 | $13,000 | $14,000 | $15,000 | $17,500 | $20,000 | $22,500 |
|---|---|---|---|---|---|---|---|---|---|
| 31 | $289,096 | $318,006 | $346,915 | $375,825 | $404,735 | $433,644 | $505,918 | $578,192 | $650,466 |
| 32 | $298,138 | $327,952 | $357,766 | $387,580 | $417,394 | $447,207 | $521,742 | $596,277 | $670,811 |
| 33 | $307,163 | $337,879 | $368,596 | $399,312 | $430,028 | $460,744 | $537,535 | $614,326 | $691,117 |
| 34 | $316,170 | $347,787 | $379,404 | $411,021 | $442,638 | $474,255 | $553,298 | $632,341 | $711,383 |
| 35 | $325,160 | $357,676 | $390,192 | $422,708 | $455,225 | $487,741 | $569,031 | $650,321 | $731,611 |
| 36 | $334,133 | $367,547 | $400,960 | $434,373 | $467,786 | $501,200 | $584,733 | $668,266 | $751,800 |
| 37 | $343,089 | $377,398 | $411,707 | $446,015 | $480,324 | $514,633 | $600,405 | $686,178 | $771,950 |
| 38 | $352,027 | $387,230 | $422,433 | $457,635 | $492,838 | $528,041 | $616,048 | $704,054 | $792,061 |
| 39 | $360,948 | $397,043 | $433,138 | $469,233 | $505,328 | $541,423 | $631,660 | $721,897 | $812,134 |
| 40 | $369,853 | $406,838 | $443,823 | $480,808 | $517,794 | $554,779 | $647,242 | $739,705 | $832,168 |
| 41 | $378,740 | $416,614 | $454,488 | $492,362 | $530,235 | $568,109 | $662,794 | $757,479 | $852,164 |
| 42 | $387,610 | $426,371 | $465,132 | $503,892 | $542,653 | $581,414 | $678,317 | $775,219 | $872,122 |
| 43 | $396,463 | $436,109 | $475,755 | $515,401 | $555,048 | $594,694 | $693,809 | $792,925 | $892,041 |
| 44 | $405,299 | $445,828 | $486,358 | $526,888 | $567,418 | $607,948 | $709,272 | $810,597 | $911,922 |
| 45 | $414,118 | $455,529 | $496,941 | $538,353 | $579,765 | $621,176 | $724,706 | $828,235 | $931,764 |
| 46 | $422,920 | $465,212 | $507,504 | $549,795 | $592,087 | $634,379 | $740,109 | $845,839 | $951,569 |
| 47 | $431,705 | $474,875 | $518,046 | $561,216 | $604,387 | $647,557 | $755,483 | $863,410 | $971,336 |
| 48 | $440,473 | $484,520 | $528,568 | $572,615 | $616,662 | $660,710 | $770,828 | $880,946 | $991,065 |
| 49 | $449,225 | $494,147 | $539,070 | $583,992 | $628,914 | $673,837 | $786,143 | $898,449 | $1,010,755 |
| 50 | $457,959 | $503,755 | $549,551 | $595,347 | $641,143 | $686,939 | $801,429 | $915,919 | $1,030,408 |
| 51 | $466,677 | $513,345 | $560,013 | $606,680 | $653,348 | $700,016 | $816,685 | $933,354 | $1,050,024 |
| 52 | $475,378 | $522,916 | $570,454 | $617,992 | $665,530 | $713,068 | $831,912 | $950,757 | $1,069,601 |
| 53 | $484,063 | $532,469 | $580,876 | $629,282 | $677,688 | $726,094 | $847,110 | $968,126 | $1,089,142 |
| 54 | $492,731 | $542,004 | $591,277 | $640,550 | $689,823 | $739,096 | $862,279 | $985,461 | $1,108,644 |
| 55 | $501,382 | $551,520 | $601,658 | $651,797 | $701,935 | $752,073 | $877,418 | $1,002,764 | $1,128,109 |
| 56 | $510,017 | $561,018 | $612,020 | $663,021 | $714,023 | $765,025 | $892,529 | $1,020,033 | $1,147,537 |
| 57 | $518,635 | $570,498 | $622,361 | $674,225 | $726,088 | $777,952 | $907,610 | $1,037,269 | $1,166,928 |
| 58 | $527,236 | $579,960 | $632,683 | $685,407 | $738,130 | $790,854 | $922,663 | $1,054,472 | $1,186,281 |
| 59 | $535,821 | $589,403 | $642,985 | $696,567 | $750,149 | $803,731 | $937,687 | $1,071,642 | $1,205,597 |
| 60 | $544,389 | $598,828 | $653,267 | $707,706 | $762,145 | $816,584 | $952,682 | $1,088,779 | $1,224,876 |

## Starting Portfolio Needed to Fund Various Annual Expenses
### Assuming a 1% Trustee Fee (continued)

| Life Expectancies | Annual Expenses $10,000 | $11,000 | $12,000 | $13,000 | $14,000 | $15,000 | $17,500 | $20,000 | $22,500 |
|---|---|---|---|---|---|---|---|---|---|
| 61 | $552,941 | $608,236 | $663,530 | $718,824 | $774,118 | $829,412 | $967,648 | $1,105,883 | $1,244,118 |
| 62 | $561,477 | $617,625 | $673,773 | $729,920 | $786,068 | $842,216 | $982,585 | $1,122,954 | $1,263,323 |
| 63 | $569,996 | $626,996 | $683,996 | $740,995 | $797,995 | $854,995 | $997,494 | $1,139,993 | $1,282,492 |
| 64 | $578,499 | $636,349 | $694,199 | $752,049 | $809,899 | $867,749 | $1,012,374 | $1,156,998 | $1,301,623 |
| 65 | $586,986 | $645,684 | $704,383 | $763,082 | $821,780 | $880,479 | $1,027,225 | $1,173,972 | $1,320,718 |
| 66 | $595,456 | $655,002 | $714,547 | $774,093 | $833,638 | $893,184 | $1,042,048 | $1,190,912 | $1,339,776 |
| 67 | $603,910 | $664,301 | $724,692 | $785,083 | $845,474 | $905,865 | $1,056,843 | $1,207,820 | $1,358,798 |
| 68 | $612,348 | $673,583 | $734,817 | $796,052 | $857,287 | $918,522 | $1,071,609 | $1,224,696 | $1,377,783 |
| 69 | $620,769 | $682,846 | $744,923 | $807,000 | $869,077 | $931,154 | $1,086,347 | $1,241,539 | $1,396,731 |
| 70 | $629,175 | $692,092 | $755,010 | $817,927 | $880,845 | $943,762 | $1,101,056 | $1,258,350 | $1,415,644 |
| 71 | $637,564 | $701,321 | $765,077 | $828,833 | $892,590 | $956,346 | $1,115,737 | $1,275,128 | $1,434,519 |
| 72 | $645,937 | $710,531 | $775,125 | $839,719 | $904,312 | $968,906 | $1,130,390 | $1,291,875 | $1,453,359 |
| 73 | $654,295 | $719,724 | $785,153 | $850,583 | $916,012 | $981,442 | $1,145,015 | $1,308,589 | $1,472,163 |
| 74 | $662,636 | $728,899 | $795,163 | $861,426 | $927,690 | $993,953 | $1,159,612 | $1,325,271 | $1,490,930 |
| 75 | $670,961 | $738,057 | $805,153 | $872,249 | $939,345 | $1,006,441 | $1,174,181 | $1,341,921 | $1,509,662 |
| 76 | $679,270 | $747,197 | $815,124 | $883,051 | $950,978 | $1,018,905 | $1,188,722 | $1,358,540 | $1,528,357 |
| 77 | $687,563 | $756,319 | $825,076 | $893,832 | $962,588 | $1,031,344 | $1,203,235 | $1,375,126 | $1,547,017 |
| 78 | $695,840 | $765,424 | $835,008 | $904,592 | $974,176 | $1,043,760 | $1,217,720 | $1,391,680 | $1,565,640 |
| 79 | $704,102 | $774,512 | $844,922 | $915,332 | $985,742 | $1,056,152 | $1,232,178 | $1,408,203 | $1,584,228 |
| 80 | $712,347 | $783,582 | $854,816 | $926,051 | $997,286 | $1,068,520 | $1,246,607 | $1,424,694 | $1,602,781 |
| 81 | $720,577 | $792,634 | $864,692 | $936,750 | $1,008,807 | $1,080,865 | $1,261,009 | $1,441,153 | $1,621,297 |
| 82 | $728,791 | $801,670 | $874,549 | $947,428 | $1,020,307 | $1,093,186 | $1,275,383 | $1,457,581 | $1,639,779 |
| 83 | $736,989 | $810,687 | $884,386 | $958,085 | $1,031,784 | $1,105,483 | $1,289,730 | $1,473,977 | $1,658,224 |
| 84 | $745,171 | $819,688 | $894,205 | $968,722 | $1,043,239 | $1,117,756 | $1,304,049 | $1,490,342 | $1,676,635 |
| 85 | $753,338 | $828,671 | $904,005 | $979,339 | $1,054,673 | $1,130,006 | $1,318,341 | $1,506,675 | $1,695,010 |
| 86 | $761,489 | $837,637 | $913,786 | $989,935 | $1,066,084 | $1,142,233 | $1,332,605 | $1,522,977 | $1,713,349 |
| 87 | $769,624 | $846,586 | $923,549 | $1,000,511 | $1,077,474 | $1,154,436 | $1,346,842 | $1,539,248 | $1,731,654 |
| 88 | $777,744 | $855,518 | $933,292 | $1,011,067 | $1,088,841 | $1,166,616 | $1,361,051 | $1,555,487 | $1,749,923 |
| 89 | $785,848 | $864,433 | $943,017 | $1,021,602 | $1,100,187 | $1,178,772 | $1,375,234 | $1,571,696 | $1,768,158 |
| 90 | $793,936 | $873,330 | $952,724 | $1,032,117 | $1,111,511 | $1,190,905 | $1,389,389 | $1,587,873 | $1,786,357 |

**Annual Expenses**

| Life Expectancies | $25,000 | $27,500 | $30,000 | $35,000 | $40,000 | $45,000 | $50,000 |
|---|---|---|---|---|---|---|---|
| 1 | $23,992 | $26,392 | $28,791 | $33,589 | $38,388 | $43,186 | $47,985 |
| 2 | $47,939 | $52,732 | $57,526 | $67,114 | $76,702 | $86,289 | $95,877 |
| 3 | $71,839 | $79,023 | $86,207 | $100,574 | $114,942 | $129,310 | $143,678 |
| 4 | $95,693 | $105,263 | $114,832 | $133,971 | $153,109 | $172,248 | $191,387 |
| 5 | $119,502 | $131,452 | $143,402 | $167,303 | $191,203 | $215,104 | $239,004 |
| 6 | $143,265 | $157,591 | $171,918 | $200,571 | $229,224 | $257,877 | $286,530 |
| 7 | $166,982 | $183,681 | $200,379 | $233,775 | $267,172 | $300,568 | $333,965 |
| 8 | $190,654 | $209,720 | $228,785 | $266,916 | $305,047 | $343,177 | $381,308 |
| 9 | $214,280 | $235,709 | $257,137 | $299,993 | $342,849 | $385,705 | $428,561 |
| 10 | $237,862 | $261,648 | $285,434 | $333,006 | $380,578 | $428,151 | $475,723 |
| 11 | $261,397 | $287,537 | $313,677 | $365,956 | $418,236 | $470,515 | $522,795 |
| 12 | $284,888 | $313,377 | $341,865 | $398,843 | $455,821 | $512,798 | $569,776 |
| 13 | $308,333 | $339,167 | $370,000 | $431,667 | $493,333 | $555,000 | $616,667 |
| 14 | $331,734 | $364,907 | $398,081 | $464,427 | $530,774 | $597,121 | $663,468 |
| 15 | $355,090 | $390,598 | $426,107 | $497,125 | $568,143 | $639,161 | $710,179 |
| 16 | $378,400 | $416,240 | $454,080 | $529,760 | $605,440 | $681,121 | $756,801 |
| 17 | $401,666 | $441,833 | $482,000 | $562,333 | $642,666 | $722,999 | $803,333 |
| 18 | $424,888 | $467,376 | $509,865 | $594,843 | $679,820 | $764,798 | $849,775 |
| 19 | $448,064 | $492,871 | $537,677 | $627,290 | $716,903 | $806,516 | $896,129 |
| 20 | $471,197 | $518,316 | $565,436 | $659,676 | $753,915 | $848,154 | $942,394 |
| 21 | $494,285 | $543,713 | $593,142 | $691,999 | $790,856 | $889,712 | $988,569 |
| 22 | $517,328 | $569,061 | $620,794 | $724,260 | $827,725 | $931,191 | $1,034,657 |
| 23 | $540,328 | $594,360 | $648,393 | $756,459 | $864,524 | $972,590 | $1,080,655 |
| 24 | $563,283 | $619,611 | $675,939 | $788,596 | $901,253 | $1,013,909 | $1,126,566 |
| 25 | $586,194 | $644,813 | $703,433 | $820,672 | $937,911 | $1,055,149 | $1,172,388 |
| 26 | $609,061 | $669,967 | $730,874 | $852,686 | $974,498 | $1,096,310 | $1,218,123 |
| 27 | $631,885 | $695,073 | $758,261 | $884,638 | $1,011,015 | $1,137,392 | $1,263,769 |
| 28 | $654,664 | $720,130 | $785,597 | $916,530 | $1,047,462 | $1,178,395 | $1,309,328 |
| 29 | $677,400 | $745,140 | $812,880 | $948,360 | $1,083,840 | $1,219,320 | $1,354,800 |
| 30 | $700,092 | $770,101 | $840,110 | $980,129 | $1,120,147 | $1,260,166 | $1,400,184 |

## STARTING PORTFOLIO NEEDED TO FUND VARIOUS ANNUAL EXPENSES
### ASSUMING A 1% TRUSTEE FEE (CONTINUED)

| Life Expectancies | Annual Expenses $25,000 | $27,500 | $30,000 | $35,000 | $40,000 | $45,000 | $50,000 |
|---|---|---|---|---|---|---|---|
| 31 | $722,741 | $795,015 | 867288.63 | $1,011,837 | $1,156,385 | $1,300,933 | $1,445,481 |
| 32 | $745,346 | $819,880 | $894,415 | $1,043,484 | $1,192,553 | $1,341,622 | $1,490,691 |
| 33 | $767,907 | $844,698 | $921,489 | $1,075,070 | $1,228,652 | $1,382,233 | $1,535,815 |
| 34 | $790,426 | $869,468 | $948,511 | $1,106,596 | $1,264,681 | $1,422,766 | $1,580,852 |
| 35 | $812,901 | $894,191 | $975,481 | $1,138,061 | $1,300,642 | $1,463,222 | $1,625,802 |
| 36 | $835,333 | $918,866 | $1,002,400 | $1,169,466 | $1,336,533 | $1,503,599 | $1,670,666 |
| 37 | $857,722 | $943,494 | $1,029,266 | $1,200,811 | $1,372,355 | $1,543,900 | $1,715,444 |
| 38 | $880,068 | $968,075 | $1,056,082 | $1,232,095 | $1,408,109 | $1,584,122 | $1,760,136 |
| 39 | $902,371 | $992,608 | $1,082,845 | $1,263,320 | $1,443,794 | $1,624,268 | $1,804,742 |
| 40 | $924,631 | $1,017,095 | $1,109,558 | $1,294,484 | $1,479,410 | $1,664,337 | $1,849,263 |
| 41 | $946,849 | $1,041,534 | $1,136,219 | $1,325,589 | $1,514,959 | $1,704,328 | $1,893,698 |
| 42 | $969,024 | $1,065,926 | $1,162,829 | $1,356,634 | $1,550,438 | $1,744,243 | $1,938,048 |
| 43 | $991,156 | $1,090,272 | $1,189,388 | $1,387,619 | $1,585,850 | $1,784,082 | $1,982,313 |
| 44 | $1,013,246 | $1,114,571 | $1,215,896 | $1,418,545 | $1,621,194 | $1,823,843 | $2,026,493 |
| 45 | $1,035,294 | $1,138,823 | $1,242,353 | $1,449,411 | $1,656,470 | $1,863,529 | $2,070,588 |
| 46 | $1,057,299 | $1,163,029 | $1,268,759 | $1,480,219 | $1,691,678 | $1,903,138 | $2,114,598 |
| 47 | $1,079,262 | $1,187,188 | $1,295,114 | $1,510,967 | $1,726,819 | $1,942,672 | $2,158,524 |
| 48 | $1,101,183 | $1,211,301 | $1,321,419 | $1,541,656 | $1,761,892 | $1,982,129 | $2,202,366 |
| 49 | $1,123,062 | $1,235,368 | $1,347,674 | $1,572,286 | $1,796,898 | $2,021,511 | $2,246,123 |
| 50 | $1,144,898 | $1,259,388 | $1,373,878 | $1,602,858 | $1,831,837 | $2,060,817 | $2,289,797 |
| 51 | $1,166,693 | $1,283,362 | $1,400,032 | $1,633,370 | $1,866,709 | $2,100,048 | $2,333,386 |
| 52 | $1,188,446 | $1,307,291 | $1,426,135 | $1,663,824 | $1,901,514 | $2,139,203 | $2,376,892 |
| 53 | $1,210,157 | $1,331,173 | $1,452,189 | $1,694,220 | $1,936,252 | $2,178,283 | $2,420,315 |
| 54 | $1,231,827 | $1,355,010 | $1,478,192 | $1,724,558 | $1,970,923 | $2,217,288 | $2,463,654 |
| 55 | $1,253,455 | $1,378,800 | $1,504,146 | $1,754,837 | $2,005,528 | $2,256,219 | $2,506,910 |
| 56 | $1,275,041 | $1,402,545 | $1,530,050 | $1,785,058 | $2,040,066 | $2,295,074 | $2,550,083 |
| 57 | $1,296,586 | $1,426,245 | $1,555,904 | $1,815,221 | $2,074,538 | $2,333,855 | $2,593,173 |
| 58 | $1,318,090 | $1,449,899 | $1,581,708 | $1,845,326 | $2,108,944 | $2,372,562 | $2,636,180 |
| 59 | $1,339,552 | $1,473,508 | $1,607,463 | $1,875,373 | $2,143,284 | $2,411,194 | $2,679,105 |
| 60 | $1,360,974 | $1,497,071 | $1,633,168 | $1,905,363 | $2,177,558 | $2,449,752 | $2,721,947 |

**Annual Expenses**

| Life Expectancies | $25,000 | $27,500 | $30,000 | $35,000 | $40,000 | $45,000 | $50,000 |
|---|---|---|---|---|---|---|---|
| 61 | $1,382,354 | $1,520,589 | $1,658,824 | $1,935,295 | $2,211,766 | $2,488,237 | $2,764,707 |
| 62 | $1,403,693 | $1,544,062 | $1,684,431 | $1,965,170 | $2,245,908 | $2,526,647 | $2,807,385 |
| 63 | $1,424,991 | $1,567,490 | $1,709,989 | $1,994,987 | $2,279,985 | $2,564,984 | $2,849,982 |
| 64 | $1,446,248 | $1,590,873 | $1,735,498 | $2,024,747 | $2,313,997 | $2,603,246 | $2,892,496 |
| 65 | $1,467,464 | $1,614,211 | $1,760,957 | $2,054,450 | $2,347,943 | $2,641,436 | $2,934,929 |
| 66 | $1,488,640 | $1,637,504 | $1,786,368 | $2,084,096 | $2,381,824 | $2,679,552 | $2,977,280 |
| 67 | $1,509,775 | $1,660,753 | $1,811,730 | $2,113,685 | $2,415,640 | $2,717,595 | $3,019,550 |
| 68 | $1,530,870 | $1,683,957 | $1,837,044 | $2,143,218 | $2,449,392 | $2,755,565 | $3,061,739 |
| 69 | $1,551,924 | $1,707,116 | $1,862,308 | $2,172,693 | $2,483,078 | $2,793,463 | $3,103,847 |
| 70 | $1,572,937 | $1,730,231 | $1,887,525 | $2,202,112 | $2,516,700 | $2,831,287 | $3,145,875 |
| 71 | $1,593,911 | $1,753,302 | $1,912,693 | $2,231,475 | $2,550,257 | $2,869,039 | $3,187,821 |
| 72 | $1,614,844 | $1,776,328 | $1,937,812 | $2,260,781 | $2,583,750 | $2,906,718 | $3,229,687 |
| 73 | $1,635,736 | $1,799,310 | $1,962,884 | $2,290,031 | $2,617,178 | $2,944,325 | $3,271,473 |
| 74 | $1,656,589 | $1,822,248 | $1,987,907 | $2,319,225 | $2,650,542 | $2,981,860 | $3,313,178 |
| 75 | $1,677,402 | $1,845,142 | $2,012,882 | $2,348,362 | $2,683,843 | $3,019,323 | $3,354,803 |
| 76 | $1,698,174 | $1,867,992 | $2,037,809 | $2,377,444 | $2,717,079 | $3,056,714 | $3,396,349 |
| 77 | $1,718,907 | $1,890,798 | $2,062,689 | $2,406,470 | $2,750,252 | $3,094,033 | $3,437,815 |
| 78 | $1,739,600 | $1,913,560 | $2,087,520 | $2,435,441 | $2,783,361 | $3,131,281 | $3,479,201 |
| 79 | $1,760,254 | $1,936,279 | $2,112,305 | $2,464,355 | $2,816,406 | $3,168,457 | $3,520,508 |
| 80 | $1,780,867 | $1,958,954 | $2,137,041 | $2,493,214 | $2,849,388 | $3,205,561 | $3,561,735 |
| 81 | $1,801,442 | $1,981,586 | $2,161,730 | $2,522,018 | $2,882,307 | $3,242,595 | $3,602,883 |
| 82 | $1,821,976 | $2,004,174 | $2,186,372 | $2,550,767 | $2,915,162 | $3,279,557 | $3,643,953 |
| 83 | $1,842,472 | $2,026,719 | $2,210,966 | $2,579,460 | $2,947,954 | $3,316,449 | $3,684,943 |
| 84 | $1,862,927 | $2,049,220 | $2,235,513 | $2,608,098 | $2,980,684 | $3,353,269 | $3,725,855 |
| 85 | $1,883,344 | $2,071,679 | $2,260,013 | $2,636,682 | $3,013,351 | $3,390,019 | $3,766,688 |
| 86 | $1,903,722 | $2,094,094 | $2,284,466 | $2,665,210 | $3,045,954 | $3,426,699 | $3,807,443 |
| 87 | $1,924,060 | $2,116,466 | $2,308,872 | $2,693,684 | $3,078,496 | $3,463,308 | $3,848,120 |
| 88 | $1,944,359 | $2,138,795 | $2,333,231 | $2,722,103 | $3,110,975 | $3,499,847 | $3,888,718 |
| 89 | $1,964,620 | $2,161,082 | $2,357,543 | $2,750,467 | $3,143,391 | $3,536,315 | $3,929,239 |
| 90 | $1,984,841 | $2,183,325 | $2,381,809 | $2,778,777 | $3,175,746 | $3,572,714 | $3,969,682 |

# Preparation for Attorney Meeting

# Preparation For Attorney Meeting

Planning for your child's life after your death necessarily involves legal documents—typically wills and trusts. A will is necessary so you can make sure your property goes to the right people, in the proportions that you want. A trust is necessary to receive the property that you want to reserve for your child with a disability, so as to permit proper management and avoid loss of government benefits.

Completing the following form will help you get your thoughts in order before you see your attorney. You may change your mind about certain items after your initial meeting as your attorney may raise issues you do not consider yourself. So you should treat the form as a first attempt to deal with some very difficult questions.

## GENERAL INFORMATION

Most attorney's require information similar to the following before preparing an estate plan. Having this information ready before your initial visit will save both time and money.

### FULL NAME

Father _____

Mother _____

### DATE OF BIRTH

Father _____

Mother _____

### SOCIAL SECURITY NUMBER

Father _____

Mother _____

### ADDRESS

_____

_____

### HOME PHONE

_____

### WORK PHONE

Father _____

Mother _____

### OCCUPATION

Father _____

Mother _____

### ANNUAL INCOME

Father _____

Mother _____

## INFORMATION ABOUT CHILDREN WITHOUT DISABILITIES

1.  Full Name _____ Age _____ Phone # _____

    Address _____

    If child is married or has children list name of spouse and names and ages of each child. If the child is an adult and you have concerns about the child's ability to manage money, mention that as well.

    _____

    _____

    _____

2.  Full Name _____ Age _____ Phone # _____

    Address _____

    If child is married or has children list name of spouse and names and ages of each child. If the child is an adult and you have concerns about the child's ability to manage money, mention that as well.

    _____

    _____

    _____

3.  Full Name _____ Age _____ Phone # _____

    Address _____

    If child is married or has children list name of spouse and names and ages of each child. If the child is an adult and you have concerns about the child's ability to manage money, mention that as well.

    _____

    _____

    _____

4.  Full Name _____ Age _____ Phone # _____

    Address _____

     If child is married or has children list name of spouse and names and ages of each child. If the child is an adult and you have concerns about the child's ability to manage money, mention that as well.

_____

_____

_____

5.  Full Name _____ Age _____ Phone # _____

    Address _____

     If child is married or has children list name of spouse and names and ages of each child. If the child is an adult and you have concerns about the child's ability to manage money, mention that as well.

_____

_____

_____

6.  Full Name _____ Age _____ Phone # _____

    Address _____

     If child is married or has children list name of spouse and names and ages of each child. If the child is an adult and you have concerns about the child's ability to manage money, mention that as well.

_____

_____

_____

## INFORMATION ABOUT CHILDREN WITH DISABILITIES

1. Full Name _____ Age _____ Phone # _____

   Address _____

   Briefly describe the nature of your child's disability. Include information relating to your child's ability to manage money properly. If child is married or has children, list names of spouse and names and ages of each child.

   _____

   _____

   _____

   _____

   _____

   _____

2. Full Name _____ Age _____ Phone # _____

   Address _____

   Briefly describe the nature of your child's disability. Include information relating to your child's ability to manage money properly. If child is married or has children, list names of spouse and names and ages of each child.

   _____

   _____

   _____

   _____

## FORMER MARRIAGES

If either of you was formerly married, list names of former spouse and any children from former marriage.

_____

_____

_____

## CRITICAL PEOPLE

### EXECUTOR

The executor will be responsible for paying your debts (including burial expenses) and for collecting your assets and distributing them in accordance with the provisions contained in your will. The executor may also be responsible for filing estate and income tax returns. List in order of preference the people and institutions that you would like to serve as your executor. Include names, the person's relationship to you (for example, spouse, son, brother, friend...), and the person's age, phone number and address.

**Mother**

1. Full Name _____ Age _____ Relationship _____

   Address _____ Phone # _____

2. Full Name _____ Age _____ Relationship _____

   Address _____ Phone # _____

3. Full Name _____ Age _____ Relationship _____

   Address _____ Phone # _____

**Father**

1. Full Name _____ Age _____ Relationship _____

   Address _____ Phone # _____

2. Full Name _____ Age _____ Relationship _____

   Address _____ Phone # _____

3. Full Name _____ Age _____ Relationship _____

   Address _____ Phone # _____

## GUARDIANS FOR MINOR CHILDREN

A guardian is the person appointed to care for your child if you die before your child reaches the age of majority. Guardians do not act until both parents die and are necessary both for children with disabilities and those without disabilities. List in order of preference the people that you would like to serve as guardian for your minor children. Include names, the person's relationship to you (for example: spouse, son, brother, friend...), the person's phone number, and the person's address.

1. Full Name _____ Age _____ Relationship _____

   Address _____ Phone # _____

2. Full Name _____ Age _____ Relationship _____

   Address _____ Phone # _____

3. Full Name _____ Age _____ Relationship _____

   Address _____ Phone # _____

## GUARDIANS FOR ADULTS WITH DISABILITIES

The law presumes that individuals over the age of eighteen (in some states, twenty-one) are competent; that is, that they are able to make their own decisions about what is best for them in their daily lives. This means that, as a legal matter, no matter how severe the disability may be, your child will have the right to make his or her own decisions about the future upon reaching the age of majority. If your child is now over eighteen and if a guardian has not been appointed, your child already has that right.

This presumption of competence can be overcome only by a court of law in what has come to be known as a "guardianship proceeding." You should not automatically assume that a guardian is necessary for your child. The issue is discussed in detail in the book *Planning For The Future*.

1. Has a guardian been appointed by a court for your adult child? If a guardian has been appointed, be sure to bring the court order appointing the guardian with you when you meet with your attorney.

   ❏ yes        ❏ no

2. If a guardian has been appointed for your adult child, list the guardian's name, age, phone number and address. If co-guardians have been appointed, list both names.

   (a) Full Name _____ Age _____ Relationship _____

   Address _____ Phone # _____

   (b) Full Name _____ Age _____ Relationship _____

   Address _____ Phone # _____

3. If a guardian has been appointed for your adult child and successor guardians have been appointed by the court as well, list their names, ages, phone numbers and addresses in the order in which they are to act.

    (a) Full Name _____ Age _____ Relationship _____

        Address _____ Phone # _____

    (b) Full Name _____ Age _____ Relationship _____

        Address _____ Phone # _____

4. If a guardian has not been appointed for your adult child, list in order of preference the people that you would like to serve as guardian should guardianship prove necessary in the future. Include names, the person's relationship to you (for example: spouse, son, brother, friend...), and the person's age, phone number and address.

    (a) Full Name _____ Age _____ Relationship _____

        Address _____ Phone # _____

    (b) Full Name _____ Age _____ Relationship _____

        Address _____ Phone # _____

    (c) Full Name _____ Age _____ Relationship _____

        Address _____ Phone # _____

    (d) Full Name _____ Age _____ Relationship _____

        Address _____ Phone # _____

## TRUSTEES

The trustee is the person who will be responsible for managing your child's money. You can use individuals or institutions. Many people appoint co-trustees to increase the chance that their child's interests will be protected. It is even possible to name an individual to act with a bank. The bank takes care of the money management responsibilities, and the individual can look out for your child's personal needs.

List in order of preference the people and institutions that you would like to serve as trustee. Include names, ages, phone numbers, the person's relationship to you, and the person's address. Because the trust will last for your child's entire lifetime, several possibilities should be considered. Be prepared to discuss with your attorney whether you want to have the trustees act by themselves, or whether you would prefer some type of co-trustee arrangement.

### INDIVIDUALS

(1) Full Name _____ Age _____ Relationship _____

Address _____ Phone # _____

(2) Full Name _____ Age _____ Relationship _____

Address _____ Phone # _____

(3) Full Name _____ Age _____ Relationship _____

Address _____ Phone # _____

(4) Full Name _____ Age _____ Relationship _____

Address _____ Phone # _____

(5) Full Name _____ Age _____ Relationship _____

Address _____ Phone # _____

(6) Full Name _____ Age _____ Relationship _____

Address _____ Phone # _____

### INSTITUTIONS

(1) Full Name _____

Address _____ Phone # _____

(2) Full Name _____

Address _____ Phone # _____

## POWER OF ATTORNEY FOR HEALTHCARE

You can use a power of attorney for healthcare in many states to appoint an agent to make healthcare decisions for you if you are not able to do so. List in order of preference the people you would like to appoint, include complete names and addresses. Most people put their spouse as first choice and friends or other family members thereafter.

(1) Full Name _____ Age _____ Relationship _____

Address _____ Phone # _____

(2) Full Name _____ Age _____ Relationship _____

Address _____ Phone # _____

(3) Full Name _____ Age _____ Relationship _____

Address _____ Phone # _____

(4) Full Name _____ Age _____ Relationship _____

Address _____ Phone # _____

# DISPOSITION OF PROPERTY

## PERSONAL PROPERTY

List any specific preferences you have in regard to your personal property (items such as jewelry, pictures, automobiles, crystal....). We generally find that it is best not to go overboard in the list as things tend to work best if your heirs divide personal property as they choose.

If you are married, the personal bequests tend not to take effect until the death of the survivor of you. If you would like particular bequests to take effect before your spouse dies, you should say so specifically.

_____

_____

_____

_____

_____

## RESIDUAL PROPERTY

Your residual property is all property that is not personal. Typically this includes assets such as bank accounts, money markets, stocks, bonds, annuities, mutual funds, retirement accounts and your home, as well as any other items of property which you may own.

1. If you are married and your spouse survives you, would you like all your property to go to your spouse?

   **mother**   ❏ yes  ❏ no      **father**   ❏ yes  ❏ no

2. If you are married and the answer to 1 is yes, list how you want your property to be divided when you and your spouse have both died. If you are not married, you should list how you want your property to be divided when you die. Possibilities include dividing your property between your children in specified percentages, or anything else you consider appropriate.

_____

_____

_____

_____

_____

_____

_____

_____

_____

_____

_____

3. If you are married and the answer to question 1 is no, list how you would like your property to be divided, again assuming your spouse survives you.

_____

_____

_____

_____

_____

## TRUST REMAINDER

As stated above, in most cases estate plans created by families that have a member with a disability involve the creation of a trust both to manage the inheritance of the person with a disability and to maintain eligibility for government benefits. State how you would like any remaining property to be distributed when your child dies. In particular, you should think about your feelings if your child has children of his or her own. You should also think about whether you want your child to have the ability to say where any remaining property should go. Many families choose to leave a portion of any property that remains in their child's trust to charitable organizations that may have helped the child during his or her life. If you wish to do so, name the charity or charities and the percentage that you would like to leave to each of them. Other possibilities include dividing your property between your other children in specified percentages, or anything else you consider appropriate.

_____

_____

_____

_____

_____

_____

## BUSINESS ASSETS

If you own your own business, list your thoughts about how it should be run after your death. Be sure to list the names, phone numbers and addresses of the people who should run it. Also list the names, phone numbers and addresses of people who are critical to business operations.

_____

_____

_____

_____

_____

_____

_____

_____

_____

_____

1.  Full Name _____ Age _____ Phone # _____

    Address _____

2.  Full Name _____ Age _____ Phone # _____

    Address _____

3.  Full Name _____ Age _____ Phone # _____

    Address _____

## FINANCIAL ASSETS

To do a thorough estate plan, your attorney will need a general understanding of the size and character of your estate. Exact values are not required. You should complete the following form if you have not already done so. The form is also included in Part Two.

### CHART TWO—FAMILY BALANCE SHEET

| Assets | Joint | Father | Mother |
|---|---|---|---|
| Residence | $ _____ | _____ | _____ |
| Other real estate | $ _____ | _____ | _____ |
| Bank accounts | $ _____ | _____ | _____ |
| Retirement accounts | $ _____ | _____ | _____ |
| CD's | $ _____ | _____ | _____ |
| Annuities | $ _____ | _____ | _____ |
| Stocks, securities | $ _____ | _____ | _____ |
| Business interests | $ _____ | _____ | _____ |
| Other assets | $ _____ | _____ | _____ |
| **Liabilities** | | | |
| Mortgage debt | $ _____ | _____ | _____ |
| Other debt | $ _____ | _____ | _____ |

**Current Family Net Worth** (current assets less current liabilities)        $ _____

| Life Insurance | Joint | Father | Mother |
|---|---|---|---|
| Death benefit | $ _____ | _____ | _____ |
| Premiums | $ _____ | _____ | _____ |
| Cash value | $ _____ | _____ | _____ |

**Potential Inheritances**        $ _____        _____        _____

**Future Expectancies** (death benefits plus inheritances)        $ _____

**Total** (current family net worth plus future expectancies)        $ _____

THE LIFE PLANNING WORKBOOK

# Estate Plan Organizer

THE LIFE PLANNING WORKBOOK

# Estate Plan Organizer

T HE ESTATE PLAN ORGANIZER CAN BE A VALUABLE SOURCE OF INFORMATION FOR LOCATING IMPORTANT DOCU-ments and financial assets. This will ease the burden on your executor, and provide a smooth transition for your child.

## PROFESSIONALS TO CONTACT IN THE EVENT OF DEATH

Information relating to names, addresses and phone numbers of guardians, executors and trustees has been listed in Part Three. Information relating to names, addresses and phone numbers of friends, relatives and others who can help your child with a disability has been listed in Part One. Obviously these people will need to be contacted in the event of your death.

Information relating to financial and legal advisors will be helpful as well. Please complete the following.

## ATTORNEYS

Name _____ Phone # _____

Address _____

Name _____ Phone # _____

Address _____

Name _____ Phone # _____

Address _____

# LIFE INSURANCE AGENTS

Name _____ Phone # _____

Address _____

Name _____ Phone # _____

Address _____

Name _____ Phone # _____

Address _____

# FINANCIAL ADVISORS

Name _____ Phone # _____

Address _____

Name _____ Phone # _____

Address _____

Name _____ Phone # _____

Address _____

# TAX ADVISORS

Name _____ Phone # _____

Address _____

Name _____ Phone # _____

Address _____

# COMPANY EMPLOYEE BENEFITS DIRECTORS

Name _____ Phone # _____

Address _____

Name _____ Phone # _____

Address _____

Name _____ Phone # _____

Address _____

Name _____ Phone # _____

Address _____

# OTHER ADVISORS

Name _____ Phone # _____

Address _____

Name _____ Phone # _____

Address _____

Name _____ Phone # _____

Address _____

Name _____ Phone # _____

Address _____

Name _____ Phone # _____

Address _____

Name _____ Phone # _____

Address _____

# FINAL ARRANGEMENTS

Name of father _____

This is a letter of direction to my executor regarding my own final arrangements.

For my final arrangements I prefer:

_____ Burial     ❏ Location _____

                    ❏ Location Unknown

_____ Cremation     ❏ Where ashes should be placed _____

                    ❏ Unknown

Regarding a final service:

Religious     ❏ Yes (if yes, type of religion) _____

                  ❏ No (if no, type of service desired) _____

                       _____

                       _____

Specific funeral home _____

Specific cemetery _____

Prepaid/insurance _____

Military benefits _____

Other specific details or comments _____

_____

_____     _____
Date                              Signed

# FINAL ARRANGEMENTS

Name of mother _____

This is a letter of direction to my executor regarding my own final arrangements.

For my final arrangements I prefer:

_____ Burial    ❏ Location _____

               ❏ Location Unknown

_____ Cremation    ❏ Where ashes should be placed _____

               ❏ Unknown

Regarding a final service:

     Religious    ❏ Yes (if yes, type of religion) _____

               ❏ No (if no, type of service desired) _____

               _____

               _____

Specific funeral home _____

Specific cemetery _____

Prepaid/insurance _____

Military benefits _____

Other specific details or comments _____

_____

_____     _____
Date                Signed

# LOCATION OF CRITICAL DOCUMENTS RELATING TO PARENTS

| Document | Location |
|---|---|
| **Wills** | |
| **Trusts** | |
| **Power of attorney for healthcare** | |
| **Power of attorney for property** | |
| **Living will** | |
| **Marriage certificate** | |
| **Birth certificate** | |
| **Insurance policies** | |
| **Home mortgage and ownership** | |
| **Automobile title and insurance** | |
| **Tax returns** | |

# LOCATION OF CRITICAL DOCUMENTS RELATING TO PERSON WITH DISABILITY

| Document | Location |
|---|---|
| Medical records | |
| Individual education plan | |
| Individual program plan | |
| Individual habilitation plan | |
| Diagnostic testing reports | |
| Psychological reports | |
| Information about special equipment | |
| Residential admission papers | |
| Residential investigatory papers | |
| Records related to employment | |
| Guardianship papers | |
| Government benefit papers | |
| Information relating to advocacy organizations | |
| Certificates and awards | |
| Recipes for favored foods | |

# LOCATION OF OTHER IMPORTANT DOCUMENTS

| Document | Location |
|----------|----------|
|          |          |
|          |          |
|          |          |
|          |          |
|          |          |
|          |          |
|          |          |
|          |          |
|          |          |
|          |          |
|          |          |
|          |          |
|          |          |

ESTATE PLAN ORGANIZER

# SAFE DEPOSIT BOXES

Bank _____

Address _____

Phone number _____

Location of keys _____

Persons authorized to sign _____

Box number _____

Contents _____

_____

_____

_____


Bank _____

Address _____

Phone number _____

Location of keys _____

Persons authorized to sign _____

Box number _____

Contents _____

_____

_____

_____

# BANK ACCOUNTS AND CERTIFICATES OF DEPOSIT

Name of bank _____

Account number _____

Address _____

Phone number _____

Names of those authorized to sign _____

Location of checkbook or passbook _____

---

Name of bank _____

Account number _____

Address _____

Phone number _____

Names of those authorized to sign _____

Location of checkbook or passbook _____

---

Name of bank _____

Account number _____

Address _____

Phone number _____

Names of those authorized to sign _____

Location of checkbook or passbook _____

# BANK ACCOUNTS AND CERTIFICATES OF DEPOSIT

Name of bank _____

Account number _____

Address _____

Phone number _____

Names of those authorized to sign _____

Location of checkbook or passbook _____


Name of bank _____

Account number _____

Address _____

Phone number _____

Names of those authorized to sign _____

Location of checkbook or passbook _____


Name of bank _____

Account number _____

Address _____

Phone number _____

Names of those authorized to sign _____

Location of checkbook or passbook _____

# BANK ACCOUNTS AND CERTIFICATES OF DEPOSIT

Name of bank _____

Account number _____

Address _____

Phone number _____

Names of those authorized to sign _____

Location of checkbook or passbook _____


Name of bank _____

Account number _____

Address _____

Phone number _____

Names of those authorized to sign _____

Location of checkbook or passbook _____


Name of bank _____

Account number _____

Address _____

Phone number _____

Names of those authorized to sign _____

Location of checkbook or passbook _____

# BANK ACCOUNTS AND CERTIFICATES OF DEPOSIT

Name of bank _____

Account number _____

Address _____

Phone number _____

Names of those authorized to sign _____

Location of checkbook or passbook _____

Name of bank _____

Account number _____

Address _____

Phone number _____

Names of those authorized to sign _____

Location of checkbook or passbook _____

Name of bank _____

Account number _____

Address _____

Phone number _____

Names of those authorized to sign _____

Location of checkbook or passbook _____

# MUTUAL FUNDS, BROKERAGE ACCOUNTS AND MONEY MARKET ACCOUNTS

Name of institution _____

Account number _____

Address _____

Phone number _____

Names of those authorized to sign _____

Name, address and phone number of broker _____

_____

Location of records _____

---

Name of institution _____

Account number _____

Address _____

Phone number _____

Names of those authorized to sign _____

Name, address and phone number of broker _____

_____

Location of records _____

# MUTUAL FUNDS, BROKERAGE ACCOUNTS AND MONEY MARKET ACCOUNTS

Name of institution _____

Account number _____

Address _____

Phone number _____

Names of those authorized to sign _____

Name, address and phone number of broker _____

_____

Location of records _____

---

Name of institution _____

Account number _____

Address _____

Phone number _____

Names of those authorized to sign _____

Name, address and phone number of broker _____

_____

Location of records _____

# MUTUAL FUNDS, BROKERAGE ACCOUNTS AND MONEY MARKET ACCOUNTS

Name of institution _____

Account number _____

Address _____

Phone number _____

Names of those authorized to sign _____

Name, address and phone number of broker _____

_____

Location of records _____

---

Name of institution _____

Account number _____

Address _____

Phone number _____

Names of those authorized to sign _____

Name, address and phone number of broker _____

_____

Location of records _____

# MUTUAL FUNDS, BROKERAGE ACCOUNTS AND MONEY MARKET ACCOUNTS

Name of institution _____

Account number _____

Address _____

Phone number _____

Names of those authorized to sign _____

Name, address and phone number of broker _____

_____

Location of records _____

Name of institution _____

Account number _____

Address _____

Phone number _____

Names of those authorized to sign _____

Name, address and phone number of broker _____

_____

Location of records _____

# ANNUITIES

Name of institution _____

Account number _____

Address _____

Phone number _____

Name of owner _____

Name of beneficiary _____

Name, address and phone number of broker _____

_____

Location of records _____

Name of institution _____

Account number _____

Address _____

Phone number _____

Name of owner _____

Name of beneficiary _____

Name, address and phone number of broker _____

_____

Location of records _____

# ANNUITIES

Name of institution _____

Account number _____

Address _____

Phone number _____

Name of owner _____

Name of beneficiary _____

Name, address and phone number of broker _____

_____

Location of records _____

Name of institution _____

Account number _____

Address _____

Phone number _____

Name of owner _____

Name of beneficiary _____

Name, address and phone number of broker _____

_____

Location of records _____

# INDIVIDUAL RETIREMENT ACCOUNTS, 401(K)'S AND OTHER RETIREMENT ACCOUNTS

Name of institution _____

Account number _____

Address _____

Phone number _____

Name of owner _____

Name of beneficiary _____

Name, address and phone number of broker _____

_____

Location of records _____

Name of institution _____

Account number _____

Address _____

Phone number _____

Name of owner _____

Name of beneficiary _____

Name, address and phone number of broker _____

_____

Location of records _____

# INDIVIDUAL RETIREMENT ACCOUNTS, 401(K)'S AND OTHER RETIREMENT ACCOUNTS

Name of institution _____

Account number _____

Address _____

Phone number _____

Name of owner _____

Name of beneficiary _____

Name, address and phone number of broker _____

_____

Location of records _____

Name of institution _____

Account number _____

Address _____

Phone number _____

Name of owner _____

Name of beneficiary _____

Name, address and phone number of broker _____

_____

Location of records _____

# Individual Retirement Accounts, 401(k)'s and Other Retirement Accounts

Name of institution _____

Account number _____

Address _____

Phone number _____

Name of owner _____

Name of beneficiary _____

Name, address and phone number of broker _____

_____

Location of records _____

Name of institution _____

Account number _____

Address _____

Phone number _____

Name of owner _____

Name of beneficiary _____

Name, address and phone number of broker _____

_____

Location of records _____

# Individual Retirement Accounts, 401(k)'s and Other Retirement Accounts

Name of institution _____

Account number _____

Address _____

Phone number _____

Name of owner _____

Name of beneficiary _____

Name, address and phone number of broker _____

_____

Name of institution _____

Account number _____

Address _____

Phone number _____

Name of owner _____

Name of beneficiary _____

Name, address and phone number of broker _____

_____

Location of records _____

# LIFE INSURANCE POLICIES

Name of insurance company _____

Policy number _____ Phone number _____

Address _____

Name of owner _____

Name of beneficiary _____

Name, address and phone number of agent _____

_____

Type of policy _____ Date issued _____

Death benefit _____ Loans outstanding _____

Location of policy _____

Name of insurance company _____

Policy number _____ Phone number _____

Address _____

Name of owner _____

Name of beneficiary _____

Name, address and phone number of agent _____

_____

Type of policy _____ Date issued _____

Death benefit _____ Loans outstanding _____

Location of policy _____

# LIFE INSURANCE POLICIES

Name of insurance company _____

Policy number _____ Phone number _____

Address _____

Name of owner _____

Name of beneficiary _____

Name, address and phone number of agent _____

_____

Type of policy _____ Date issued _____

Death benefit _____ Loans outstanding _____

Location of policy _____

Name of insurance company _____

Policy number _____ Phone number _____

Address _____

Name of owner _____

Name of beneficiary _____

Name, address and phone number of agent _____

_____

Type of policy _____ Date issued _____

Death benefit _____ Loans outstanding _____

Location of policy _____

# LIFE INSURANCE POLICIES

Name of insurance company _____

Policy number _____ Phone number _____

Address _____

Name of owner _____

Name of beneficiary _____

Name, address and phone number of agent _____

_____

Type of policy _____ Date issued _____

Death benefit _____ Loans outstanding _____

Location of policy _____

Name of insurance company _____

Policy number _____ Phone number _____

Address _____

Name of owner _____

Name of beneficiary _____

Name, address and phone number of agent _____

_____

Type of policy _____ Date issued _____

Death benefit _____ Loans outstanding _____

Location of policy _____

# LIFE INSURANCE POLICIES

Name of insurance company _____

Policy number _____ Phone number _____

Address _____

Name of owner _____

Name of beneficiary _____

Name, address and phone number of agent _____

_____

Type of policy _____ Date issued _____

Death benefit _____ Loans outstanding _____

Location of Policy _____

---

Name of insurance company _____

Policy number _____ Phone number _____

Address _____

Name of owner _____

Name of beneficiary _____

Name, address and phone number of agent _____

_____

Type of policy _____ Date issued _____

Death benefit _____ Loans outstanding _____

Location of policy _____

# REAL ESTATE

Description _____

Address _____

Mortgage holder _____

Loan number _____

Location of records _____

Description _____

Address _____

Mortgage holder _____

Loan number _____

Location of records _____

Description _____

Address _____

Mortgage holder _____

Loan number _____

Location of records _____

# REAL ESTATE

Description _____

Address _____

Mortgage holder _____

Loan number _____

Location of records _____

Description _____

Address _____

Mortgage holder _____

Loan number _____

Location of records _____

Description _____

Address _____

Mortgage holder _____

Loan number _____

Location of records _____

# U. S. Savings Bonds

Face amount _____

Date _____

Maturity date _____

Serial number _____

Series _____

Location of certificate _____

---

Face amount _____

Date _____

Maturity date _____

Serial number _____

Series _____

Location of certificate _____

---

Face amount _____

Date _____

Maturity date _____

Serial number _____

Series _____

Location of certificate _____

# U. S. Savings Bonds

Face amount _____

Date _____

Maturity date _____

Serial number _____

Series _____

Location of certificate _____

Face amount _____

Date _____

Maturity date _____

Serial number _____

Series _____

Location of certificate _____

Face amount _____

Date _____

Maturity date _____

Serial number _____

Series _____

Location of certificate _____

# SECURITIES HELD OUTSIDE BROKERAGE ACCOUNTS

Description _____

Location of certificate _____

How is title held _____

Description _____

Location of certificate _____

How is title held _____

Description _____

Location of certificate _____

How is title held _____

Description _____

Location of certificate _____

How is title held _____

Description _____

Location of certificate _____

How is title held _____

# SECURITIES HELD OUTSIDE BROKERAGE ACCOUNTS

Description _____

Location of certificate _____

How is title held _____

Description _____

Location of certificate _____

How is title held

Description _____

Location of certificate _____

How is title held _____

Description _____

Location of certificate _____

How is title held _____

Description _____

Location of certificate _____

How is title held _____

# SECURITIES HELD OUTSIDE BROKERAGE ACCOUNTS

Description _____

Location of certificate _____

How is title held _____

Description _____

Location of certificate _____

How is title held

Description _____

Location of certificate _____

How is title held _____

Description _____

Location of certificate _____

How is title held _____

Description _____

Location of certificate _____

How is title held _____

# SECURITIES HELD OUTSIDE BROKERAGE ACCOUNTS

Description _____

Location of certificate _____

How is title held _____

Description _____

Location of certificate _____

How is title held

Description _____

Location of certificate _____

How is title held _____

Description _____

Location of certificate _____

How is title held _____

Description _____

Location of certificate _____

How is title held _____

# OTHER INSURANCE POLICIES (DISABILITY, HEALTH, PROPERTY, CASUALTY, LIABILITY)

Type of Insurance _____

Name of insurance company _____

Policy number _____

Address _____

Phone number _____

Name, address and phone number of agent _____

_____

Location of policy _____

Type of Insurance _____

Name of insurance company _____

Policy number _____

Address _____

Phone number _____

Name, address and phone number of agent _____

_____

Location of policy _____

# OTHER INSURANCE POLICIES (DISABILITY, HEALTH, PROPERTY, CASUALTY, LIABILITY)

Type of insurance _____

Name of insurance company _____

Policy number _____

Address _____

Phone number _____

Name, address and phone number of agent _____

_____

Location of policy _____

Type of insurance _____

Name of insurance company _____

Policy number _____

Address _____

Phone number _____

Name, address and phone number of agent _____

_____

Location of policy _____

# OTHER INSURANCE POLICIES (DISABILITY, HEALTH, PROPERTY, CASUALTY, LIABILITY)

Type of insurance _____

Name of insurance company _____

Policy number _____

Address _____

Phone number _____

Name, address and phone number of agent _____

_____

Location of policy _____

Type of insurance _____

Name of insurance company _____

Policy number _____

Address _____

Phone number _____

Name, address and phone number of agent _____

_____

Location of policy _____

# OTHER INSURANCE POLICIES (DISABILITY, HEALTH, PROPERTY, CASUALTY, LIABILITY)

Type of insurance _____

Name of insurance company _____

Policy number _____

Address _____

Phone number _____

Name, address and phone number of agent _____

_____

Location of policy _____

Type of insurance _____

Name of insurance company _____

Policy number _____

Address _____

Phone number _____

Name, address and phone number of agent _____

_____

Location of policy _____

# OTHER ASSETS

Description _____

Contact person (include phone number and address) _____

_____

Location of records _____

Additional information _____

---

Description _____

Contact person (include phone number and address) _____

_____

Location of records _____

Additional information _____

---

Description _____

Contact person (include phone number and address) _____

_____

Location of records _____

Additional information _____

# OTHER ASSETS

Description _____

Contact person (include phone number and address) _____

_____

Location of records _____

Additional information _____

Description _____

Contact person (include phone number and address) _____

_____

Location of records _____

Additional information _____

Description _____

Contact person (include phone number and address) _____

_____

Location of records _____

Additional information _____

# OTHER ASSETS

Description _____

Contact person (include phone number and address) _____

_____

Location of records _____

Additional information _____

Description _____

Contact person (include phone number and address) _____

_____

Location of records _____

Additional information _____

Description _____

Contact person (include phone number and address) _____

_____

Location of records _____

Additional information _____

# OTHER ASSETS

Description _____

Contact person (include phone number and address) _____

_____

Location of records _____

Additional information _____

Description _____

Contact person (include phone number and address) _____

_____

Location of records _____

Additional information _____

Description _____

Contact person (include phone number and address) _____

_____

Location of records _____

Additional information _____

## LIABILITIES (CREDIT CARD BALANCES, MORTGAGES, TAXES, OTHER)

Description _____

Person or institution owed _____

Contact person (include phone number and address) _____

_____

Location of records _____

Additional information _____

Description _____

Person or institution owed _____

Contact person (include phone number and address) _____

_____

Location of records _____

Additional information _____

Description _____

Person or institution owed _____

Contact person (include phone number and address) _____

_____

Location of records _____

Additional information _____

# LIABILITIES (CREDIT CARD BALANCES, MORTGAGES, TAXES, OTHER)

Description _____

Person or institution owed _____

Contact person (include phone number and address) _____

_____

Location of records _____

Additional information _____

---

Description _____

Person or institution owed _____

Contact person (include phone number and address) _____

_____

Location of records _____

Additional information _____

---

Description _____

Person or institution owed _____

Contact person (include phone number and address) _____

_____

Location of records _____

Additional information _____

# Liabilities (Credit card balances, mortgages, taxes, other)

Description _____

Person or institution owed _____

Contact person (include phone number and address) _____

_____

Location of records _____

Additional information _____

Description _____

Person or institution owed _____

Contact person (include phone number and address) _____

_____

Location of records _____

Additional information _____

Description _____

Person or institution owed _____

Contact person (include phone number and address) _____

_____

Location of records _____

Additional information _____

# LIABILITIES (CREDIT CARD BALANCES, MORTGAGES, TAXES, OTHER)

Description _____

Person or institution owed _____

Contact person (include phone number and address) _____

_____

Location of records _____

Additional information _____

Description _____

Person or institution owed _____

Contact person (include phone number and address) _____

_____

Location of records _____

Additional information _____

Description _____

Person or institution owed _____

Contact person (include phone number and address) _____

_____

Location of records _____

Additional information _____

# Supplemental Financial Needs Analysis for Financial Professionals

THE LIFE PLANNING WORKBOOK

# Supplemental Financial Needs Analysis for Financial Professional

AS DESCRIBED PREVIOUSLY, THE CALCULATIONS IN Part Two of the main text require assumptions as to rates of return and taxes. While we believe the assumptions to be reasonable for the reasons previously outlined, you may be interested in how the calculations differ if different assumptions are made. The information contained in this appendix is complicated, and is probably unnecessary for most families. We include it only for the sake of completeness, and as a resource for financial professionals and others who are expert in financial matters.

Chart One shows the amount required to fund $1,000 of expenses over varying life expectancies with varying projected rates of return assuming no taxes or trustee fees. Charts Two, Three and Four are the same as Chart One except they assume tax rates of ten percent, twenty percent and thirty percent respectively.

Chart Five shows the amount required to fund $1,000 of expenses over varying life expectancies with varying projected rates of return assuming a one percent trustee fee and no taxes. Charts Six, Seven and Eight are the same as Chart Five except they assume tax rates of ten percent, twenty percent and thirty percent respectively.

The example below illustrates how to use the charts to see how varying assumptions affect the calculation of a child's financial needs.

## EXAMPLE

John and Mary complete parts one, two and three of Chart One of Part Two in the main text and determine that their 39-year-old son, Sam, will need $250 per month to fund his needs. This figure is multiplied by 12 to get Sam's annual needs— $3,000. John and Mary are not concerned about trustee fees because they trust John's sister to handle his finances.

John and Mary then go to Chart Three of Part Two and determine that as a 39-year-old male, Sam has a life expectancy of another 41 years, and they add 10 years to be sure the trust fund is sufficient. In the example contained in Part Two, we assumed a 6.5 percent rate of return, a twenty percent tax rate and no trustee fees. Turning to the 6.5 percent return rate on Chart Three of this appendix (which assumes no trustee fee and a twenty percent tax rate), we see that $36,912 is necessary to provide $1,000 per year for 51 years (multiplying by 3 we get $110,736 to provide $3,000 per year which was the answer derived in the text). If we assume a 7.5 percent rate of return, Chart Three tells us we need $31,073 to provide $1,000 per year for 51 years or $93,219 to provide $3,000 per year.

Chart One provides the required information if we assume a zero percent tax rate, Chart Two assumes a ten percent tax rate and Chart Four assumes a thirty percent tax rate. Charts Five, Six, Seven and Eight provide the same information assuming a one percent trustee fee. Chart Five assumes a zero percent tax rate, Chart Six assumes a ten percent rate, Chart Seven assumes a twenty percent tax rate and Chart Eight assumes a thirty percent tax rate.

# CHART ONE

## STARTING PORTFOLIO NEEDED TO FUND VARIOUS ANNUAL EXPENSES ASSUMING NO TRUSTEE FEE AND 0% TAX RATE

**Inputs**

| | | | | | | | | | | | | | |
|---|---|---|---|---|---|---|---|---|---|---|---|---|
| R=real rate of return | 0.0% | 0.5% | 1.0% | 1.5% | 2.0% | 2.5% | 3.0% | 3.5% | 4.0% | 4.5% | 5.0% | 5.5% | 6.0% |
| T=tax rate | 0.0% | | | | | | | | | | | | |
| A=annual admin. fee | 0.0% | | | | | | | | | | | | |
| I=inflation | 4.0% | | | | | | | | | | | | |
| E=expenses to start (ann) | 1.04 / $1,000 | 1.045 / $1,000 | 1.05 / $1,000 | 1.055 / $1,000 | 1.06 / $1,000 | 1.065 / $1,000 | 1.07 / $1,000 | 1.075 / $1,000 | 1.08 / $1,000 | 1.085 / $1,000 | 1.09 / $1,000 | 1.095 / $1,000 | 1.1 / $1,000 |

Figures assume that expenses are all taken out at end of each year.

**Rate of Return (Nominal):**

| Life Expectancies | 4.0% | 4.5% | 5.0% | 5.5% | 6.0% | 6.5% | 7.0% | 7.5% | 8.0% | 8.5% | 9.0% | 9.5% | 10.0% |
|---|---|---|---|---|---|---|---|---|---|---|---|---|---|
| 1 | $962 | $957 | $952 | $948 | $943 | $939 | $935 | $930 | $926 | $922 | $917 | $913 | $909 |
| 2 | $1,923 | $1,909 | $1,896 | $1,882 | $1,869 | $1,856 | $1,843 | $1,830 | $1,818 | $1,805 | $1,793 | $1,781 | $1,769 |
| 3 | $2,885 | $2,857 | $2,830 | $2,803 | $2,777 | $2,751 | $2,726 | $2,701 | $2,676 | $2,652 | $2,628 | $2,604 | $2,581 |
| 4 | $3,846 | $3,800 | $3,755 | $3,711 | $3,668 | $3,626 | $3,584 | $3,543 | $3,503 | $3,464 | $3,425 | $3,387 | $3,350 |
| 5 | $4,808 | $4,739 | $4,672 | $4,606 | $4,542 | $4,480 | $4,418 | $4,358 | $4,299 | $4,242 | $4,185 | $4,130 | $4,076 |
| 6 | $5,769 | $5,673 | $5,580 | $5,489 | $5,400 | $5,313 | $5,229 | $5,146 | $5,066 | $4,987 | $4,911 | $4,836 | $4,763 |
| 7 | $6,731 | $6,603 | $6,479 | $6,359 | $6,242 | $6,128 | $6,017 | $5,909 | $5,804 | $5,702 | $5,603 | $5,506 | $5,412 |
| 8 | $7,692 | $7,529 | $7,370 | $7,216 | $7,067 | $6,923 | $6,783 | $6,647 | $6,515 | $6,387 | $6,263 | $6,143 | $6,026 |
| 9 | $8,654 | $8,449 | $8,252 | $8,061 | $7,877 | $7,699 | $7,527 | $7,361 | $7,200 | $7,044 | $6,893 | $6,747 | $6,606 |
| 10 | $9,615 | $9,366 | $9,126 | $8,895 | $8,672 | $8,457 | $8,251 | $8,051 | $7,859 | $7,674 | $7,495 | $7,322 | $7,155 |
| 11 | $10,577 | $10,278 | $9,991 | $9,716 | $9,452 | $9,198 | $8,954 | $8,719 | $8,494 | $8,277 | $8,068 | $7,867 | $7,674 |
| 12 | $11,538 | $11,186 | $10,849 | $10,526 | $10,217 | $9,921 | $9,637 | $9,366 | $9,105 | $8,855 | $8,616 | $8,385 | $8,164 |
| 13 | $12,500 | $12,089 | $11,698 | $11,324 | $10,967 | $10,627 | $10,302 | $9,991 | $9,694 | $9,410 | $9,138 | $8,877 | $8,628 |
| 14 | $13,462 | $12,988 | $12,539 | $12,111 | $11,704 | $11,316 | $10,948 | $10,596 | $10,261 | $9,941 | $9,636 | $9,345 | $9,067 |
| 15 | $14,423 | $13,883 | $13,372 | $12,887 | $12,426 | $11,990 | $11,575 | $11,181 | $10,807 | $10,450 | $10,111 | $9,789 | $9,481 |
| 16 | $15,385 | $14,774 | $14,197 | $13,651 | $13,135 | $12,647 | $12,185 | $11,747 | $11,332 | $10,939 | $10,565 | $10,210 | $9,873 |
| 17 | $16,346 | $15,660 | $15,014 | $14,405 | $13,831 | $13,289 | $12,778 | $12,295 | $11,839 | $11,407 | $10,998 | $10,611 | $10,244 |
| 18 | $17,308 | $16,542 | $15,823 | $15,148 | $14,513 | $13,916 | $13,354 | $12,825 | $12,326 | $11,855 | $11,411 | $10,991 | $10,594 |
| 19 | $18,269 | $17,420 | $16,625 | $15,880 | $15,183 | $14,529 | $13,915 | $13,338 | $12,795 | $12,285 | $11,805 | $11,352 | $10,925 |
| 20 | $19,231 | $18,293 | $17,419 | $16,603 | $15,840 | $15,127 | $14,459 | $13,834 | $13,247 | $12,697 | $12,181 | $11,695 | $11,238 |
| 21 | $20,192 | $19,163 | $18,205 | $17,314 | $16,484 | $15,711 | $14,988 | $14,314 | $13,683 | $13,092 | $12,539 | $12,021 | $11,534 |
| 22 | $21,154 | $20,028 | $18,984 | $18,016 | $17,117 | $16,281 | $15,503 | $14,778 | $14,102 | $13,471 | $12,882 | $12,330 | $11,814 |
| 23 | $22,115 | $20,889 | $19,756 | $18,708 | $17,737 | $16,837 | $16,003 | $15,227 | $14,506 | $13,834 | $13,208 | $12,624 | $12,079 |

## Inputs

| | |
|---|---|
| R=real rate of return | 0.0% |
| T=tax rate | 0.0% |
| A=annual admin. fee | 0.0% |
| I=inflation | 4.0% |

| | 0.0% | 0.5% | 1.0% | 1.5% | 2.0% | 2.5% | 3.0% | 3.5% | 4.0% | 4.5% | 5.0% | 5.5% | 6.0% |
|---|---|---|---|---|---|---|---|---|---|---|---|---|---|
| | 1.04 | 1.045 | 1.05 | 1.055 | 1.06 | 1.065 | 1.07 | 1.075 | 1.08 | 1.085 | 1.09 | 1.095 | 1.1 |
| E=expenses to start (ann) | $1,000 | $1,000 | $1,000 | $1,000 | $1,000 | $1,000 | $1,000 | $1,000 | $1,000 | $1,000 | $1,000 | $1,000 | $1,000 |

Figures assume that expenses are all taken out at end of each year.

| Rate of Return (Nominal): | 4.0% | 4.5% | 5.0% | 5.5% | 6.0% | 6.5% | 7.0% | 7.5% | 8.0% | 8.5% | 9.0% | 9.5% | 10.0% |
|---|---|---|---|---|---|---|---|---|---|---|---|---|---|
| **Life Expectancies** | | | | | | | | | | | | | |
| 24 | $23,077 | $21,746 | $20,520 | $19,390 | $18,346 | $17,381 | $16,488 | $15,661 | $14,894 | $14,182 | $13,520 | $12,903 | $12,329 |
| 25 | $24,038 | $22,599 | $21,277 | $20,062 | $18,943 | $17,912 | $16,961 | $16,082 | $15,269 | $14,515 | $13,817 | $13,169 | $12,566 |
| 26 | $25,000 | $23,448 | $22,027 | $20,724 | $19,529 | $18,431 | $17,420 | $16,488 | $15,629 | $14,835 | $14,101 | $13,420 | $12,790 |
| 27 | $25,962 | $24,292 | $22,769 | $21,378 | $20,104 | $18,937 | $17,866 | $16,882 | $15,976 | $15,141 | $14,371 | $13,660 | $13,001 |
| 28 | $26,923 | $25,133 | $23,505 | $22,022 | $20,668 | $19,431 | $18,300 | $17,262 | $16,310 | $15,435 | $14,629 | $13,887 | $13,201 |
| 29 | $27,885 | $25,970 | $24,234 | $22,656 | $21,222 | $19,914 | $18,721 | $17,631 | $16,632 | $15,717 | $14,876 | $14,102 | $13,390 |
| 30 | $28,846 | $26,803 | $24,955 | $23,282 | $21,765 | $20,386 | $19,131 | $17,987 | $16,942 | $15,986 | $15,111 | $14,307 | $13,569 |
| 31 | $29,808 | $27,631 | $25,670 | $23,899 | $22,297 | $20,846 | $19,529 | $18,331 | $17,240 | $16,245 | $15,335 | $14,502 | $13,738 |
| 32 | $30,769 | $28,456 | $26,378 | $24,507 | $22,820 | $21,296 | $19,916 | $18,665 | $17,528 | $16,493 | $15,549 | $14,687 | $13,897 |
| 33 | $31,731 | $29,277 | $27,079 | $25,106 | $23,333 | $21,735 | $20,292 | $18,987 | $17,805 | $16,731 | $15,753 | $14,862 | $14,049 |
| 34 | $32,692 | $30,094 | $27,773 | $25,697 | $23,836 | $22,164 | $20,658 | $19,299 | $18,071 | $16,958 | $15,948 | $15,029 | $14,191 |
| 35 | $33,654 | $30,907 | $28,461 | $26,280 | $24,330 | $22,582 | $21,013 | $19,601 | $18,328 | $17,177 | $16,134 | $15,187 | $14,326 |
| 36 | $34,615 | $31,716 | $29,143 | $26,854 | $24,814 | $22,991 | $21,359 | $19,893 | $18,575 | $17,386 | $16,311 | $15,338 | $14,454 |
| 37 | $35,577 | $32,521 | $29,817 | $27,420 | $25,289 | $23,390 | $21,694 | $20,176 | $18,813 | $17,586 | $16,480 | $15,481 | $14,575 |
| 38 | $36,538 | $33,322 | $30,486 | $27,978 | $25,755 | $23,780 | $22,021 | $20,449 | $19,042 | $17,779 | $16,642 | $15,616 | $14,689 |
| 39 | $37,500 | $34,120 | $31,148 | $28,528 | $26,213 | $24,161 | $22,338 | $20,714 | $19,263 | $17,963 | $16,796 | $15,745 | $14,797 |
| 40 | $38,462 | $34,913 | $31,804 | $29,070 | $26,662 | $24,533 | $22,646 | $20,969 | $19,475 | $18,140 | $16,943 | $15,868 | $14,899 |
| 41 | $39,423 | $35,703 | $32,453 | $29,605 | $27,102 | $24,896 | $22,946 | $21,217 | $19,680 | $18,309 | $17,083 | $15,984 | $14,995 |
| 42 | $40,385 | $36,489 | $33,096 | $30,132 | $27,534 | $25,251 | $23,237 | $21,456 | $19,877 | $18,471 | $17,217 | $16,094 | $15,086 |
| 43 | $41,346 | $37,272 | $33,734 | $30,651 | $27,958 | $25,597 | $23,520 | $21,688 | $20,067 | $18,627 | $17,345 | $16,199 | $15,173 |
| 44 | $42,308 | $38,050 | $34,365 | $31,163 | $28,374 | $25,935 | $23,795 | $21,912 | $20,249 | $18,776 | $17,466 | $16,299 | $15,254 |
| 45 | $43,269 | $38,825 | $34,990 | $31,668 | $28,782 | $26,265 | $24,063 | $22,129 | $20,425 | $18,919 | $17,583 | $16,393 | $15,331 |
| 46 | $44,231 | $39,596 | $35,609 | $32,166 | $29,182 | $26,587 | $24,323 | $22,339 | $20,595 | $19,056 | $17,694 | $16,483 | $15,404 |

# Chart One

## Starting Portfolio Needed to Fund Various Annual Expenses Assuming No Trustee Fee and 0% Tax Rate (continued)

**Inputs**

| | | | | | | | | | | | | | | |
|---|---|---|---|---|---|---|---|---|---|---|---|---|---|---|
| R=real rate of return | 0.0% | | | | | | | | | | | | | |
| T=tax rate | 0.0% | | | | | | | | | | | | | |
| A=annual admin. fee | 0.0% | | | | | | | | | | | | | |
| I=inflation | 4.0% | | | | | | | | | | | | | |
| | | 0.0% | 0.5% | 1.0% | 1.5% | 2.0% | 2.5% | 3.0% | 3.5% | 4.0% | 4.5% | 5.0% | 5.5% | 6.0% |
| | | 1.04 | 1.045 | 1.05 | 1.055 | 1.06 | 1.065 | 1.07 | 1.075 | 1.08 | 1.085 | 1.09 | 1.095 | 1.1 |
| E=expenses to start (ann) | | $1,000 | $1,000 | $1,000 | $1,000 | $1,000 | $1,000 | $1,000 | $1,000 | $1,000 | $1,000 | $1,000 | $1,000 | $1,000 |

Figures assume that expenses are all taken out at end of each year.

**Rate of Return (Nominal):**

| Life Expectancies | 4.0% | 4.5% | 5.0% | 5.5% | 6.0% | 6.5% | 7.0% | 7.5% | 8.0% | 8.5% | 9.0% | 9.5% | 10.0% |
|---|---|---|---|---|---|---|---|---|---|---|---|---|---|
| 47 | $45,192 | $40,364 | $36,222 | $32,656 | $29,575 | $26,902 | $24,575 | $22,542 | $20,758 | $19,187 | $17,799 | $16,568 | $15,473 |
| 48 | $46,154 | $41,128 | $36,830 | $33,140 | $29,960 | $27,210 | $24,821 | $22,738 | $20,915 | $19,313 | $17,900 | $16,649 | $15,538 |
| 49 | $47,115 | $41,888 | $37,431 | $33,617 | $30,339 | $27,510 | $25,059 | $22,928 | $21,066 | $19,434 | $17,997 | $16,726 | $15,599 |
| 50 | $48,077 | $42,644 | $38,027 | $34,087 | $30,709 | $27,803 | $25,291 | $23,112 | $21,212 | $19,549 | $18,089 | $16,800 | $15,658 |
| 51 | $49,038 | $43,397 | $38,617 | $34,550 | $31,073 | $28,089 | $25,517 | $23,289 | $21,352 | $19,660 | $18,176 | $16,869 | $15,713 |
| 52 | $50,000 | $44,147 | $39,202 | $35,006 | $31,431 | $28,369 | $25,736 | $23,461 | $21,487 | $19,767 | $18,260 | $16,935 | $15,765 |
| 53 | $50,962 | $44,892 | $39,781 | $35,457 | $31,781 | $28,642 | $25,949 | $23,628 | $21,617 | $19,868 | $18,340 | $16,998 | $15,814 |
| 54 | $51,923 | $45,634 | $40,354 | $35,900 | $32,125 | $28,909 | $26,156 | $23,789 | $21,743 | $19,966 | $18,416 | $17,057 | $15,860 |
| 55 | $52,885 | $46,373 | $40,922 | $36,338 | $32,462 | $29,169 | $26,357 | $23,944 | $21,863 | $20,060 | $18,489 | $17,114 | $15,904 |
| 56 | $53,846 | $47,108 | $41,485 | $36,769 | $32,793 | $29,423 | $26,553 | $24,095 | $21,980 | $20,149 | $18,558 | $17,167 | $15,946 |
| 57 | $54,808 | $47,840 | $42,042 | $37,194 | $33,118 | $29,672 | $26,743 | $24,241 | $22,091 | $20,235 | $18,624 | $17,218 | $15,985 |
| 58 | $55,769 | $48,568 | $42,594 | $37,613 | $33,436 | $29,914 | $26,928 | $24,382 | $22,199 | $20,318 | $18,687 | $17,267 | $16,022 |
| 59 | $56,731 | $49,292 | $43,141 | $38,026 | $33,749 | $30,151 | $27,107 | $24,518 | $22,303 | $20,397 | $18,747 | $17,313 | $16,058 |
| 60 | $57,692 | $50,013 | $43,683 | $38,433 | $34,055 | $30,382 | $27,282 | $24,650 | $22,403 | $20,472 | $18,805 | $17,356 | $16,091 |
| 61 | $58,654 | $50,731 | $44,219 | $38,835 | $34,356 | $30,608 | $27,452 | $24,778 | $22,499 | $20,545 | $18,860 | $17,398 | $16,122 |
| 62 | $59,615 | $51,445 | $44,750 | $39,231 | $34,651 | $30,828 | $27,617 | $24,901 | $22,592 | $20,615 | $18,912 | $17,437 | $16,152 |
| 63 | $60,577 | $52,156 | $45,276 | $39,621 | $34,941 | $31,044 | $27,777 | $25,021 | $22,681 | $20,681 | $18,962 | $17,474 | $16,180 |
| 64 | $61,538 | $52,863 | $45,798 | $40,005 | $35,225 | $31,254 | $27,933 | $25,136 | $22,767 | $20,745 | $19,009 | $17,510 | $16,207 |
| 65 | $62,500 | $53,567 | $46,314 | $40,384 | $35,504 | $31,459 | $28,084 | $25,248 | $22,849 | $20,806 | $19,055 | $17,544 | $16,232 |
| 66 | $63,462 | $54,268 | $46,825 | $40,758 | $35,777 | $31,660 | $28,231 | $25,356 | $22,929 | $20,865 | $19,098 | $17,576 | $16,255 |
| 67 | $64,423 | $54,965 | $47,332 | $41,126 | $36,046 | $31,855 | $28,374 | $25,461 | $23,006 | $20,921 | $19,140 | $17,606 | $16,278 |
| 68 | $65,385 | $55,659 | $47,833 | $41,489 | $36,309 | $32,047 | $28,513 | $25,562 | $23,080 | $20,975 | $19,179 | $17,635 | $16,299 |
| 69 | $66,346 | $56,350 | $48,330 | $41,847 | $36,567 | $32,233 | $28,648 | $25,660 | $23,151 | $21,027 | $19,217 | $17,663 | $16,319 |

THE LIFE PLANNING WORKBOOK

## Inputs

| | | | | | | | | | | | | | |
|---|---|---|---|---|---|---|---|---|---|---|---|---|---|
| R=real rate of return | 0.0% | 0.5% | 1.0% | 1.5% | 2.0% | 2.5% | 3.0% | 3.5% | 4.0% | 4.5% | 5.0% | 5.5% | 6.0% |
| T=tax rate | 0.0% | | | | | | | | | | | | |
| A=annual admin. fee | 0.0% | | | | | | | | | | | | |
| I=inflation | 4.0% | | | | | | | | | | | | |
| | 1.04 | 1.045 | 1.05 | 1.055 | 1.06 | 1.065 | 1.07 | 1.075 | 1.08 | 1.085 | 1.09 | 1.095 | 1.1 |
| E=expenses to start (ann) | $1,000 | $1,000 | $1,000 | $1,000 | $1,000 | $1,000 | $1,000 | $1,000 | $1,000 | $1,000 | $1,000 | $1,000 | $1,000 |

Figures assume that expenses are all taken out at end of each year.

| Rate of Return (Nominal): | 4.0% | 4.5% | 5.0% | 5.5% | 6.0% | 6.5% | 7.0% | 7.5% | 8.0% | 8.5% | 9.0% | 9.5% | 10.0% |
|---|---|---|---|---|---|---|---|---|---|---|---|---|---|
| **Life Expectancies** | | | | | | | | | | | | | |
| 70 | $67,308 | $57,037 | $48,822 | $42,200 | $36,821 | $32,416 | $28,780 | $25,755 | $23,219 | $21,077 | $19,253 | $17,689 | $16,338 |
| 71 | $68,269 | $57,721 | $49,309 | $42,548 | $37,069 | $32,594 | $28,907 | $25,847 | $23,285 | $21,124 | $19,287 | $17,713 | $16,356 |
| 72 | $69,231 | $58,402 | $49,792 | $42,891 | $37,313 | $32,767 | $29,032 | $25,936 | $23,349 | $21,170 | $19,320 | $17,737 | $16,373 |
| 73 | $70,192 | $59,079 | $50,270 | $43,229 | $37,553 | $32,937 | $29,152 | $26,021 | $23,410 | $21,213 | $19,351 | $17,759 | $16,389 |
| 74 | $71,154 | $59,754 | $50,744 | $43,562 | $37,788 | $33,103 | $29,269 | $26,104 | $23,469 | $21,255 | $19,381 | $17,781 | $16,404 |
| 75 | $72,115 | $60,425 | $51,213 | $43,891 | $38,018 | $33,265 | $29,383 | $26,185 | $23,525 | $21,295 | $19,409 | $17,801 | $16,418 |
| 76 | $73,077 | $61,092 | $51,678 | $44,215 | $38,244 | $33,423 | $29,494 | $26,262 | $23,580 | $21,334 | $19,436 | $17,820 | $16,432 |
| 77 | $74,038 | $61,757 | $52,138 | $44,534 | $38,466 | $33,577 | $29,602 | $26,338 | $23,633 | $21,371 | $19,462 | $17,838 | $16,445 |
| 78 | $75,000 | $62,419 | $52,594 | $44,849 | $38,683 | $33,728 | $29,706 | $26,410 | $23,683 | $21,406 | $19,487 | $17,855 | $16,457 |
| 79 | $75,962 | $63,077 | $53,045 | $45,159 | $38,897 | $33,875 | $29,808 | $26,481 | $23,732 | $21,440 | $19,510 | $17,872 | $16,468 |
| 80 | $76,923 | $63,732 | $53,492 | $45,465 | $39,106 | $34,019 | $29,907 | $26,549 | $23,779 | $21,472 | $19,533 | $17,887 | $16,479 |
| 81 | $77,885 | $64,384 | $53,935 | $45,766 | $39,312 | $34,160 | $30,003 | $26,615 | $23,824 | $21,503 | $19,554 | $17,902 | $16,489 |
| 82 | $78,846 | $65,033 | $54,374 | $46,063 | $39,514 | $34,297 | $30,096 | $26,678 | $23,868 | $21,533 | $19,575 | $17,916 | $16,499 |
| 83 | $79,808 | $65,679 | $54,809 | $46,356 | $39,712 | $34,431 | $30,187 | $26,740 | $23,910 | $21,562 | $19,594 | $17,929 | $16,508 |
| 84 | $80,769 | $66,321 | $55,239 | $46,645 | $39,906 | $34,561 | $30,275 | $26,800 | $23,950 | $21,589 | $19,613 | $17,942 | $16,517 |
| 85 | $81,731 | $66,961 | $55,665 | $46,930 | $40,096 | $34,689 | $30,361 | $26,857 | $23,989 | $21,615 | $19,631 | $17,954 | $16,525 |
| 86 | $82,692 | $67,597 | $56,088 | $47,210 | $40,283 | $34,814 | $30,444 | $26,913 | $24,026 | $21,641 | $19,647 | $17,966 | $16,533 |
| 87 | $83,654 | $68,231 | $56,506 | $47,487 | $40,466 | $34,935 | $30,525 | $26,967 | $24,062 | $21,665 | $19,664 | $17,976 | $16,540 |
| 88 | $84,615 | $68,861 | $56,920 | $47,760 | $40,646 | $35,054 | $30,604 | $27,019 | $24,097 | $21,688 | $19,679 | $17,987 | $16,547 |
| 89 | $85,577 | $69,489 | $57,330 | $48,028 | $40,823 | $35,170 | $30,681 | $27,070 | $24,131 | $21,710 | $19,694 | $17,997 | $16,553 |
| 90 | $86,538 | $70,113 | $57,737 | $48,293 | $40,996 | $35,284 | $30,755 | $27,119 | $24,163 | $21,731 | $19,708 | $18,006 | $16,560 |

**APPENDIX ONE**

## Chart Two

### Starting Portfolio Needed to Fund Various Annual Expenses Assuming No Trustee Fee and 10% Tax Rate

**Inputs**

- R = real rate of return
- T = tax rate: 10%
- A = annual admin. fee: 0%
- I = inflation: 4%

| R = real rate of return | 0.0% | 0.5% | 1.0% | 1.5% | 2.0% | 2.5% | 3.0% | 3.5% | 4.0% | 4.5% | 5.0% | 5.5% | 6.0% |
|---|---|---|---|---|---|---|---|---|---|---|---|---|---|
| | 1.036 | 1.0405 | 1.045 | 1.0495 | 1.054 | 1.0585 | 1.063 | 1.0675 | 1.072 | 1.0765 | 1.081 | 1.0855 | 1.09 |
| E = expenses to start (ann) | $1,000 | $1,000 | $1,000 | $1,000 | $1,000 | $1,000 | $1,000 | $1,000 | $1,000 | $1,000 | $1,000 | $1,000 | $1,000 |

Figures assume that expenses are all taken out at end of each year.

| Rate of Return (Nominal): Life Expectancies | 4.0% | 4.5% | 5.0% | 5.5% | 6.0% | 6.5% | 7.0% | 7.5% | 8.0% | 8.5% | 9.0% | 9.5% | 10.0% |
|---|---|---|---|---|---|---|---|---|---|---|---|---|---|
| 1 | $965 | $961 | $957 | $953 | $949 | $945 | $941 | $937 | $933 | $929 | $925 | $921 | $917 |
| 2 | $1,934 | $1,922 | $1,909 | $1,897 | $1,885 | $1,873 | $1,861 | $1,849 | $1,838 | $1,826 | $1,815 | $1,804 | $1,793 |
| 3 | $2,907 | $2,882 | $2,857 | $2,833 | $2,809 | $2,785 | $2,762 | $2,739 | $2,716 | $2,693 | $2,671 | $2,649 | $2,628 |
| 4 | $3,883 | $3,842 | $3,800 | $3,760 | $3,720 | $3,681 | $3,643 | $3,605 | $3,568 | $3,531 | $3,495 | $3,460 | $3,425 |
| 5 | $4,864 | $4,801 | $4,739 | $4,679 | $4,619 | $4,561 | $4,504 | $4,449 | $4,394 | $4,340 | $4,288 | $4,236 | $4,185 |
| 6 | $5,848 | $5,760 | $5,673 | $5,589 | $5,507 | $5,426 | $5,348 | $5,271 | $5,196 | $5,122 | $5,050 | $4,980 | $4,911 |
| 7 | $6,836 | $6,718 | $6,603 | $6,491 | $6,383 | $6,276 | $6,173 | $6,072 | $5,973 | $5,877 | $5,784 | $5,692 | $5,603 |
| 8 | $7,827 | $7,676 | $7,529 | $7,386 | $7,246 | $7,111 | $6,980 | $6,852 | $6,728 | $6,607 | $6,489 | $6,375 | $6,263 |
| 9 | $8,823 | $8,633 | $8,449 | $8,271 | $8,099 | $7,932 | $7,770 | $7,612 | $7,460 | $7,312 | $7,168 | $7,029 | $6,893 |
| 10 | $9,822 | $9,590 | $9,366 | $9,149 | $8,940 | $8,738 | $8,542 | $8,353 | $8,170 | $7,993 | $7,821 | $7,655 | $7,495 |
| 11 | $10,825 | $10,546 | $10,278 | $10,019 | $9,770 | $9,530 | $9,298 | $9,075 | $8,859 | $8,651 | $8,450 | $8,256 | $8,068 |
| 12 | $11,832 | $11,502 | $11,186 | $10,882 | $10,589 | $10,308 | $10,038 | $9,778 | $9,527 | $9,286 | $9,054 | $8,831 | $8,616 |
| 13 | $12,843 | $12,458 | $12,089 | $11,736 | $11,397 | $11,073 | $10,761 | $10,463 | $10,176 | $9,900 | $9,636 | $9,382 | $9,138 |
| 14 | $13,858 | $13,413 | $12,988 | $12,583 | $12,195 | $11,824 | $11,469 | $11,130 | $10,805 | $10,494 | $10,196 | $9,910 | $9,636 |
| 15 | $14,877 | $14,368 | $13,883 | $13,421 | $12,981 | $12,562 | $12,162 | $11,780 | $11,415 | $11,067 | $10,734 | $10,416 | $10,111 |
| 16 | $15,899 | $15,322 | $14,774 | $14,253 | $13,758 | $13,287 | $12,839 | $12,413 | $12,007 | $11,621 | $11,252 | $10,900 | $10,565 |
| 17 | $16,926 | $16,276 | $15,660 | $15,077 | $14,524 | $14,000 | $13,502 | $13,030 | $12,582 | $12,155 | $11,750 | $11,365 | $10,998 |
| 18 | $17,957 | $17,229 | $16,542 | $15,893 | $15,280 | $14,700 | $14,151 | $13,631 | $13,139 | $12,672 | $12,230 | $11,810 | $11,411 |
| 19 | $18,991 | $18,182 | $17,420 | $16,702 | $16,026 | $15,388 | $14,785 | $14,217 | $13,680 | $13,172 | $12,691 | $12,236 | $11,805 |
| 20 | $20,030 | $19,134 | $18,293 | $17,504 | $16,761 | $16,063 | $15,406 | $14,787 | $14,204 | $13,654 | $13,135 | $12,644 | $12,181 |
| 21 | $21,072 | $20,086 | $19,163 | $18,298 | $17,488 | $16,727 | $16,014 | $15,343 | $14,713 | $14,120 | $13,562 | $13,035 | $12,539 |
| 22 | $22,119 | $21,037 | $20,028 | $19,085 | $18,204 | $17,380 | $16,608 | $15,885 | $15,207 | $14,570 | $13,972 | $13,410 | $12,882 |
| 23 | $23,170 | $21,988 | $20,889 | $19,865 | $18,911 | $18,021 | $17,189 | $16,412 | $15,685 | $15,005 | $14,367 | $13,769 | $13,208 |

| | | |
|---|---|---|
| R=real rate of return | 0.0% | |
| T=tax rate | 10% | |
| A=annual admin. fee | 0% | |
| I=inflation | 4% | |

| | 0.0% | 0.5% | 1.0% | 1.5% | 2.0% | 2.5% | 3.0% | 3.5% | 4.0% | 4.5% | 5.0% | 5.5% | 6.0% |
|---|---|---|---|---|---|---|---|---|---|---|---|---|---|
| | 1.036 | 1.0405 | 1.045 | 1.0495 | 1.054 | 1.0585 | 1.063 | 1.0675 | 1.072 | 1.0765 | 1.081 | 1.0855 | 1.09 |
| E=expenses to start (ann) | $1,000 | $1,000 | $1,000 | $1,000 | $1,000 | $1,000 | $1,000 | $1,000 | $1,000 | $1,000 | $1,000 | $1,000 | $1,000 |

Figures assume that expenses are all taken out at end of each year.

| Rate of Return (Nominal): | 4.0% | 4.5% | 5.0% | 5.5% | 6.0% | 6.5% | 7.0% | 7.5% | 8.0% | 8.5% | 9.0% | 9.5% | 10.0% |
|---|---|---|---|---|---|---|---|---|---|---|---|---|---|
| **Life Expectancies** | | | | | | | | | | | | | |
| 24 | $24,224 | $22,939 | $21,746 | $20,638 | $19,609 | $18,650 | $17,758 | $16,926 | $16,150 | $15,425 | $14,748 | $14,113 | $13,520 |
| 25 | $25,283 | $23,889 | $22,599 | $21,404 | $20,297 | $19,269 | $18,315 | $17,427 | $16,601 | $15,831 | $15,113 | $14,443 | $13,817 |
| 26 | $26,346 | $24,838 | $23,448 | $22,163 | $20,976 | $19,877 | $18,859 | $17,915 | $17,038 | $16,223 | $15,465 | $14,759 | $14,101 |
| 27 | $27,413 | $25,788 | $24,292 | $22,916 | $21,646 | $20,474 | $19,392 | $18,390 | $17,462 | $16,602 | $15,804 | $15,062 | $14,371 |
| 28 | $28,484 | $26,736 | $25,133 | $23,661 | $22,307 | $21,061 | $19,913 | $18,853 | $17,874 | $16,968 | $16,129 | $15,351 | $14,629 |
| 29 | $29,559 | $27,685 | $25,970 | $24,400 | $22,960 | $21,638 | $20,423 | $19,304 | $18,273 | $17,322 | $16,443 | $15,629 | $14,876 |
| 30 | $30,639 | $28,632 | $26,803 | $25,132 | $23,604 | $22,205 | $20,922 | $19,744 | $18,661 | $17,663 | $16,744 | $15,895 | $15,111 |
| 31 | $31,722 | $29,580 | $27,631 | $25,857 | $24,239 | $22,761 | $21,410 | $20,172 | $19,036 | $17,993 | $17,034 | $16,150 | $15,335 |
| 32 | $32,810 | $30,526 | $28,456 | $26,576 | $24,866 | $23,308 | $21,887 | $20,589 | $19,401 | $18,312 | $17,313 | $16,395 | $15,549 |
| 33 | $33,902 | $31,473 | $29,277 | $27,288 | $25,484 | $23,845 | $22,354 | $20,995 | $19,755 | $18,620 | $17,581 | $16,629 | $15,753 |
| 34 | $34,998 | $32,419 | $30,094 | $27,994 | $26,094 | $24,373 | $22,811 | $21,391 | $20,098 | $18,918 | $17,840 | $16,853 | $15,948 |
| 35 | $36,098 | $33,364 | $30,907 | $28,693 | $26,697 | $24,892 | $23,259 | $21,777 | $20,431 | $19,205 | $18,088 | $17,068 | $16,134 |
| 36 | $37,203 | $34,309 | $31,716 | $29,386 | $27,291 | $25,402 | $23,696 | $22,153 | $20,754 | $19,483 | $18,327 | $17,274 | $16,311 |
| 37 | $38,312 | $35,254 | $32,521 | $30,073 | $27,877 | $25,903 | $24,124 | $22,519 | $21,067 | $19,751 | $18,557 | $17,471 | $16,480 |
| 38 | $39,425 | $36,198 | $33,322 | $30,754 | $28,456 | $26,395 | $24,543 | $22,875 | $21,371 | $20,011 | $18,778 | $17,660 | $16,642 |
| 39 | $40,543 | $37,142 | $34,120 | $31,428 | $29,026 | $26,878 | $24,953 | $23,223 | $21,666 | $20,261 | $18,991 | $17,841 | $16,796 |
| 40 | $41,664 | $38,085 | $34,913 | $32,097 | $29,590 | $27,353 | $25,353 | $23,561 | $21,952 | $20,503 | $19,196 | $18,014 | $16,943 |
| 41 | $42,790 | $39,028 | $35,703 | $32,759 | $30,145 | $27,820 | $25,746 | $23,891 | $22,229 | $20,737 | $19,393 | $18,180 | $17,083 |
| 42 | $43,921 | $39,970 | $36,489 | $33,415 | $30,694 | $28,278 | $26,129 | $24,213 | $22,499 | $20,963 | $19,583 | $18,339 | $17,217 |
| 43 | $45,056 | $40,912 | $37,272 | $34,066 | $31,235 | $28,729 | $26,505 | $24,526 | $22,760 | $21,181 | $19,765 | $18,492 | $17,345 |
| 44 | $46,195 | $41,853 | $38,050 | $34,710 | $31,769 | $29,171 | $26,872 | $24,831 | $23,013 | $21,392 | $19,940 | $18,638 | $17,466 |
| 45 | $47,339 | $42,794 | $38,825 | $35,349 | $32,295 | $29,606 | $27,231 | $25,128 | $23,259 | $21,595 | $20,109 | $18,778 | $17,583 |
| 46 | $48,487 | $43,735 | $39,596 | $35,982 | $32,815 | $30,034 | $27,583 | $25,417 | $23,498 | $21,792 | $20,271 | $18,912 | $17,694 |

APPENDIX ONE

## Chart Two

### Starting Portfolio Needed to Fund Various Annual Expenses Assuming No Trustee Fee and 10% Tax Rate (Continued)

**Inputs**

| | | | | | | | | | | | | | |
|---|---|---|---|---|---|---|---|---|---|---|---|---|---|
| R=real rate of return | 0.0% | 0.5% | 1.0% | 1.5% | 2.0% | 2.5% | 3.0% | 3.5% | 4.0% | 4.5% | 5.0% | 5.5% | 6.0% |
| T=tax rate | 10% | | | | | | | | | | | | |
| A=annual admin. fee | 0% | | | | | | | | | | | | |
| I=inflation | 4% | | | | | | | | | | | | |
| | 1.036 | 1.0405 | 1.045 | 1.0495 | 1.054 | 1.0585 | 1.063 | 1.0675 | 1.072 | 1.0765 | 1.081 | 1.0855 | 1.09 |
| E=expenses to start (ann) | $1,000 | $1,000 | $1,000 | $1,000 | $1,000 | $1,000 | $1,000 | $1,000 | $1,000 | $1,000 | $1,000 | $1,000 | $1,000 |

Figures assume that expenses are all taken out at end of each year.

| Rate of Return (Nominal): | 4.0% | 4.5% | 5.0% | 5.5% | 6.0% | 6.5% | 7.0% | 7.5% | 8.0% | 8.5% | 9.0% | 9.5% | 10.0% |
|---|---|---|---|---|---|---|---|---|---|---|---|---|---|
| **Life Expectancies** | | | | | | | | | | | | | |
| 47 | $49,639 | $44,675 | $40,364 | $36,609 | $33,328 | $30,453 | $27,927 | $25,699 | $23,729 | $21,982 | $20,428 | $19,041 | $17,799 |
| 48 | $50,796 | $45,615 | $41,128 | $37,230 | $33,834 | $30,866 | $28,263 | $25,974 | $23,954 | $22,166 | $20,578 | $19,164 | $17,900 |
| 49 | $51,957 | $46,554 | $41,888 | $37,846 | $34,334 | $31,271 | $28,592 | $26,241 | $24,172 | $22,343 | $20,723 | $19,282 | $17,997 |
| 50 | $53,123 | $47,492 | $42,644 | $38,456 | $34,826 | $31,669 | $28,914 | $26,502 | $24,383 | $22,514 | $20,862 | $19,395 | $18,089 |
| 51 | $54,294 | $48,431 | $43,397 | $39,061 | $35,312 | $32,061 | $29,230 | $26,756 | $24,588 | $22,680 | $20,996 | $19,503 | $18,176 |
| 52 | $55,468 | $49,368 | $44,147 | $39,660 | $35,792 | $32,445 | $29,538 | $27,004 | $24,787 | $22,840 | $21,124 | $19,607 | $18,260 |
| 53 | $56,648 | $50,306 | $44,892 | $40,254 | $36,266 | $32,823 | $29,839 | $27,245 | $24,980 | $22,994 | $21,248 | $19,706 | $18,340 |
| 54 | $57,832 | $51,243 | $45,634 | $40,843 | $36,733 | $33,194 | $30,135 | $27,480 | $25,167 | $23,144 | $21,367 | $19,801 | $18,416 |
| 55 | $59,020 | $52,179 | $46,373 | $41,426 | $37,193 | $33,558 | $30,423 | $27,709 | $25,348 | $23,288 | $21,482 | $19,893 | $18,489 |
| 56 | $60,214 | $53,115 | $47,108 | $42,004 | $37,648 | $33,916 | $30,706 | $27,932 | $25,525 | $23,427 | $21,592 | $19,980 | $18,558 |
| 57 | $61,411 | $54,051 | $47,840 | $42,576 | $38,097 | $34,268 | $30,982 | $28,149 | $25,695 | $23,562 | $21,698 | $20,064 | $18,624 |
| 58 | $62,614 | $54,986 | $48,568 | $43,144 | $38,540 | $34,614 | $31,252 | $28,360 | $25,861 | $23,692 | $21,800 | $20,144 | $18,687 |
| 59 | $63,821 | $55,920 | $49,292 | $43,706 | $38,976 | $34,954 | $31,517 | $28,567 | $26,022 | $23,818 | $21,899 | $20,221 | $18,747 |
| 60 | $65,032 | $56,855 | $50,013 | $44,263 | $39,408 | $35,288 | $31,776 | $28,767 | $26,178 | $23,939 | $21,993 | $20,295 | $18,805 |
| 61 | $66,249 | $57,788 | $50,731 | $44,815 | $39,833 | $35,616 | $32,029 | $28,963 | $26,330 | $24,056 | $22,084 | $20,365 | $18,860 |
| 62 | $67,470 | $58,722 | $51,445 | $45,362 | $40,253 | $35,938 | $32,277 | $29,154 | $26,476 | $24,169 | $22,172 | $20,433 | $18,912 |
| 63 | $68,695 | $59,655 | $52,156 | $45,905 | $40,667 | $36,255 | $32,519 | $29,340 | $26,619 | $24,279 | $22,256 | $20,498 | $18,962 |
| 64 | $69,926 | $60,587 | $52,863 | $46,442 | $41,075 | $36,566 | $32,756 | $29,520 | $26,757 | $24,385 | $22,337 | $20,560 | $19,009 |
| 65 | $71,161 | $61,519 | $53,567 | $46,974 | $41,478 | $36,871 | $32,988 | $29,697 | $26,891 | $24,487 | $22,415 | $20,619 | $19,055 |
| 66 | $72,401 | $62,450 | $54,268 | $47,502 | $41,876 | $37,172 | $33,215 | $29,869 | $27,021 | $24,585 | $22,490 | $20,676 | $19,098 |
| 67 | $73,646 | $63,382 | $54,965 | $48,025 | $42,269 | $37,467 | $33,437 | $30,036 | $27,148 | $24,681 | $22,562 | $20,731 | $19,140 |
| 68 | $74,896 | $64,312 | $55,659 | $48,543 | $42,656 | $37,757 | $33,655 | $30,199 | $27,270 | $24,773 | $22,631 | $20,783 | $19,179 |
| 69 | $76,150 | $65,242 | $56,350 | $49,056 | $43,038 | $38,042 | $33,867 | $30,358 | $27,389 | $24,862 | $22,698 | $20,833 | $19,217 |

## Inputs

| | | | | | | | | | | | | | |
|---|---|---|---|---|---|---|---|---|---|---|---|---|---|
| R=real rate of return | 0.0% | 0.5% | 1.0% | 1.5% | 2.0% | 2.5% | 3.0% | 3.5% | 4.0% | 4.5% | 5.0% | 5.5% | 6.0% |
| T=tax rate | 10% | | | | | | | | | | | | |
| A=annual admin. fee | 0% | | | | | | | | | | | | |
| I=inflation | 4% | | | | | | | | | | | | |
| | 1.036 | 1.0405 | 1.045 | 1.0495 | 1.054 | 1.0585 | 1.063 | 1.0675 | 1.072 | 1.0765 | 1.081 | 1.0855 | 1.09 |
| E=expenses to start (ann) | $1,000 | $1,000 | $1,000 | $1,000 | $1,000 | $1,000 | $1,000 | $1,000 | $1,000 | $1,000 | $1,000 | $1,000 | $1,000 |

Figures assume that expenses are all taken out at end of each year.

| Rate of Return (Nominal): | 4.0% | 4.5% | 5.0% | 5.5% | 6.0% | 6.5% | 7.0% | 7.5% | 8.0% | 8.5% | 9.0% | 9.5% | 10.0% |
|---|---|---|---|---|---|---|---|---|---|---|---|---|---|
| Life Expectancies | | | | | | | | | | | | | |
| 70 | $77,409 | $66,172 | $57,037 | $49,565 | $43,415 | $38,321 | $34,075 | $30,512 | $27,504 | $24,948 | $22,762 | $20,881 | $19,253 |
| 71 | $78,673 | $67,101 | $57,721 | $50,069 | $43,787 | $38,596 | $34,278 | $30,663 | $27,616 | $25,031 | $22,824 | $20,927 | $19,287 |
| 72 | $79,942 | $68,030 | $58,402 | $50,569 | $44,155 | $38,867 | $34,478 | $30,810 | $27,724 | $25,111 | $22,883 | $20,971 | $19,320 |
| 73 | $81,216 | $68,959 | $59,079 | $51,064 | $44,517 | $39,132 | $34,672 | $30,953 | $27,830 | $25,189 | $22,940 | $21,013 | $19,351 |
| 74 | $82,495 | $69,887 | $59,754 | $51,555 | $44,874 | $39,393 | $34,863 | $31,092 | $27,932 | $25,264 | $22,995 | $21,054 | $19,381 |
| 75 | $83,779 | $70,814 | $60,425 | $52,041 | $45,227 | $39,649 | $35,049 | $31,228 | $28,031 | $25,336 | $23,048 | $21,092 | $19,409 |
| 76 | $85,068 | $71,741 | $61,092 | $52,523 | $45,575 | $39,901 | $35,232 | $31,361 | $28,127 | $25,406 | $23,099 | $21,130 | $19,436 |
| 77 | $86,361 | $72,668 | $61,757 | $53,000 | $45,918 | $40,148 | $35,410 | $31,489 | $28,220 | $25,473 | $23,148 | $21,165 | $19,462 |
| 78 | $87,660 | $73,594 | $62,419 | $53,473 | $46,257 | $40,391 | $35,585 | $31,615 | $28,311 | $25,539 | $23,195 | $21,199 | $19,487 |
| 79 | $88,964 | $74,520 | $63,077 | $53,942 | $46,592 | $40,630 | $35,755 | $31,737 | $28,398 | $25,602 | $23,240 | $21,232 | $19,510 |
| 80 | $90,272 | $75,445 | $63,732 | $54,406 | $46,922 | $40,865 | $35,923 | $31,856 | $28,483 | $25,662 | $23,284 | $21,263 | $19,533 |
| 81 | $91,586 | $76,370 | $64,384 | $54,867 | $47,247 | $41,095 | $36,086 | $31,973 | $28,566 | $25,721 | $23,326 | $21,293 | $19,554 |
| 82 | $92,905 | $77,294 | $65,033 | $55,323 | $47,568 | $41,322 | $36,246 | $32,086 | $28,646 | $25,778 | $23,366 | $21,322 | $19,575 |
| 83 | $94,229 | $78,218 | $65,679 | $55,775 | $47,885 | $41,544 | $36,402 | $32,196 | $28,724 | $25,833 | $23,405 | $21,349 | $19,594 |
| 84 | $95,558 | $79,141 | $66,321 | $56,223 | $48,198 | $41,763 | $36,556 | $32,303 | $28,799 | $25,886 | $23,443 | $21,376 | $19,613 |
| 85 | $96,892 | $80,064 | $66,961 | $56,667 | $48,506 | $41,978 | $36,705 | $32,408 | $28,872 | $25,937 | $23,479 | $21,401 | $19,631 |
| 86 | $98,232 | $80,987 | $67,597 | $57,107 | $48,811 | $42,189 | $36,852 | $32,510 | $28,943 | $25,987 | $23,513 | $21,425 | $19,647 |
| 87 | $99,576 | $81,909 | $68,231 | $57,543 | $49,111 | $42,396 | $36,995 | $32,609 | $29,012 | $26,035 | $23,546 | $21,448 | $19,664 |
| 88 | $100,926 | $82,831 | $68,861 | $57,975 | $49,408 | $42,600 | $37,135 | $32,706 | $29,079 | $26,081 | $23,578 | $21,470 | $19,679 |
| 89 | $102,281 | $83,752 | $69,489 | $58,403 | $49,700 | $42,800 | $37,273 | $32,800 | $29,144 | $26,125 | $23,609 | $21,492 | $19,694 |
| 90 | $103,641 | $84,673 | $70,113 | $58,827 | $49,989 | $42,997 | $37,407 | $32,892 | $29,207 | $26,169 | $23,639 | $21,512 | $19,708 |

# CHART THREE

## STARTING PORTFOLIO NEEDED TO FUND VARIOUS ANNUAL EXPENSES ASSUMING NO TRUSTEE FEE AND 20% TAX RATE

### Inputs

| | |
|---|---|
| R=real rate of return | 0.0% |
| T=tax rate | 20.0% |
| A=annual admin. fee | 0.0% |
| I=inflation | 4.0% |

| | 0.0% | 0.5% | 1.0% | 1.5% | 2.0% | 2.5% | 3.0% | 3.5% | 4.0% | 4.5% | 5.0% | 5.5% | 6.0% |
|---|---|---|---|---|---|---|---|---|---|---|---|---|---|
| | 1.032 | 1.036 | 1.04 | 1.044 | 1.048 | 1.052 | 1.056 | 1.06 | 1.064 | 1.068 | 1.072 | 1.076 | 1.08 |
| E=expenses to start (ann) | $1,000 | $1,000 | $1,000 | $1,000 | $1,000 | $1,000 | $1,000 | $1,000 | $1,000 | $1,000 | $1,000 | $1,000 | $1,000 |

Figures assume that expenses are all taken out at end of each year.

### Rate of Return (Nominal):

| Life Expectancies | 4.0% | 4.5% | 5.0% | 5.5% | 6.0% | 6.5% | 7.0% | 7.5% | 8.0% | 8.5% | 9.0% | 9.5% | 10.0% |
|---|---|---|---|---|---|---|---|---|---|---|---|---|---|
| 1 | $969 | $965 | $962 | $958 | $954 | $951 | $947 | $943 | $940 | $936 | $933 | $929 | $926 |
| 2 | $1,945 | $1,934 | $1,923 | $1,912 | $1,901 | $1,890 | $1,880 | $1,869 | $1,858 | $1,848 | $1,838 | $1,828 | $1,818 |
| 3 | $2,930 | $2,907 | $2,885 | $2,863 | $2,841 | $2,819 | $2,798 | $2,777 | $2,756 | $2,736 | $2,716 | $2,696 | $2,676 |
| 4 | $3,921 | $3,883 | $3,846 | $3,809 | $3,773 | $3,738 | $3,703 | $3,668 | $3,634 | $3,601 | $3,568 | $3,535 | $3,503 |
| 5 | $4,921 | $4,864 | $4,808 | $4,753 | $4,699 | $4,646 | $4,594 | $4,542 | $4,492 | $4,443 | $4,394 | $4,346 | $4,299 |
| 6 | $5,928 | $5,848 | $5,769 | $5,692 | $5,617 | $5,543 | $5,471 | $5,400 | $5,331 | $5,262 | $5,196 | $5,130 | $5,066 |
| 7 | $6,943 | $6,836 | $6,731 | $6,628 | $6,528 | $6,431 | $6,335 | $6,242 | $6,150 | $6,061 | $5,973 | $5,888 | $5,804 |
| 8 | $7,966 | $7,827 | $7,692 | $7,561 | $7,433 | $7,308 | $7,186 | $7,067 | $6,951 | $6,838 | $6,728 | $6,620 | $6,515 |
| 9 | $8,996 | $8,823 | $8,654 | $8,490 | $8,330 | $8,175 | $8,024 | $7,877 | $7,734 | $7,595 | $7,460 | $7,328 | $7,200 |
| 10 | $10,035 | $9,822 | $9,615 | $9,415 | $9,221 | $9,032 | $8,849 | $8,672 | $8,500 | $8,332 | $8,170 | $8,012 | $7,859 |
| 11 | $11,082 | $10,825 | $10,577 | $10,337 | $10,105 | $9,880 | $9,662 | $9,452 | $9,248 | $9,050 | $8,859 | $8,674 | $8,494 |
| 12 | $12,137 | $11,832 | $11,538 | $11,255 | $10,982 | $10,718 | $10,463 | $10,217 | $9,979 | $9,749 | $9,527 | $9,313 | $9,105 |
| 13 | $13,200 | $12,843 | $12,500 | $12,170 | $11,852 | $11,546 | $11,251 | $10,967 | $10,694 | $10,430 | $10,176 | $9,931 | $9,694 |
| 14 | $14,271 | $13,858 | $13,462 | $13,081 | $12,716 | $12,365 | $12,028 | $11,704 | $11,392 | $11,093 | $10,805 | $10,528 | $10,261 |
| 15 | $15,351 | $14,877 | $14,423 | $13,989 | $13,573 | $13,174 | $12,793 | $12,426 | $12,075 | $11,738 | $11,415 | $11,105 | $10,807 |
| 16 | $16,439 | $15,899 | $15,385 | $14,893 | $14,423 | $13,975 | $13,546 | $13,135 | $12,743 | $12,367 | $12,007 | $11,663 | $11,332 |
| 17 | $17,535 | $16,926 | $16,346 | $15,794 | $15,268 | $14,766 | $14,287 | $13,831 | $13,395 | $12,979 | $12,582 | $12,202 | $11,839 |
| 18 | $18,640 | $17,957 | $17,308 | $16,691 | $16,105 | $15,548 | $15,018 | $14,513 | $14,033 | $13,575 | $13,139 | $12,723 | $12,326 |
| 19 | $19,754 | $18,991 | $18,269 | $17,585 | $16,936 | $16,321 | $15,737 | $15,183 | $14,656 | $14,156 | $13,680 | $13,227 | $12,795 |
| 20 | $20,876 | $20,030 | $19,231 | $18,476 | $17,761 | $17,086 | $16,446 | $15,840 | $15,266 | $14,721 | $14,204 | $13,713 | $13,247 |
| 21 | $22,006 | $21,072 | $20,192 | $19,363 | $18,580 | $17,841 | $17,144 | $16,484 | $15,861 | $15,271 | $14,713 | $14,184 | $13,683 |
| 22 | $23,146 | $22,119 | $21,154 | $20,246 | $19,392 | $18,588 | $17,831 | $17,117 | $16,443 | $15,807 | $15,207 | $14,639 | $14,102 |
| 23 | $24,294 | $23,170 | $22,115 | $21,127 | $20,199 | $19,327 | $18,508 | $17,737 | $17,012 | $16,329 | $15,685 | $15,078 | $14,506 |

THE LIFE PLANNING WORKBOOK

## Inputs

| | |
|---|---|
| R=real rate of return | 0.0% |
| T=tax rate | 20.0% |
| A=annual admin. fee | 0.0% |
| I=inflation | 4.0% |

| | 0.0% | 0.5% | 1.0% | 1.5% | 2.0% | 2.5% | 3.0% | 3.5% | 4.0% | 4.5% | 5.0% | 5.5% | 6.0% |
|---|---|---|---|---|---|---|---|---|---|---|---|---|---|
| | 1.032 | 1.036 | 1.04 | 1.044 | 1.048 | 1.052 | 1.056 | 1.06 | 1.064 | 1.068 | 1.072 | 1.076 | 1.08 |
| E=expenses to start (ann) | $1,000 | $1,000 | $1,000 | $1,000 | $1,000 | $1,000 | $1,000 | $1,000 | $1,000 | $1,000 | $1,000 | $1,000 | $1,000 |

Figures assume that expenses are all taken out at end of each year.

| Rate of Return (Nominal): | 4.0% | 4.5% | 5.0% | 5.5% | 6.0% | 6.5% | 7.0% | 7.5% | 8.0% | 8.5% | 9.0% | 9.5% | 10.0% |
|---|---|---|---|---|---|---|---|---|---|---|---|---|---|
| Life Expectancies | | | | | | | | | | | | | |
| 24 | $25,452 | $24,224 | $23,077 | $22,003 | $20,999 | $20,057 | $19,174 | $18,346 | $17,568 | $16,837 | $16,150 | $15,503 | $14,894 |
| 25 | $26,618 | $25,283 | $24,038 | $22,877 | $21,792 | $20,779 | $19,831 | $18,943 | $18,112 | $17,332 | $16,601 | $15,914 | $15,269 |
| 26 | $27,793 | $26,346 | $25,000 | $23,747 | $22,580 | $21,492 | $20,477 | $19,529 | $18,643 | $17,814 | $17,038 | $16,311 | $15,629 |
| 27 | $28,978 | $27,413 | $25,962 | $24,614 | $23,362 | $22,198 | $21,114 | $20,104 | $19,162 | $18,283 | $17,462 | $16,695 | $15,976 |
| 28 | $30,172 | $28,484 | $26,923 | $25,478 | $24,138 | $22,895 | $21,741 | $20,668 | $19,670 | $18,740 | $17,874 | $17,065 | $16,310 |
| 29 | $31,374 | $29,559 | $27,885 | $26,338 | $24,908 | $23,585 | $22,359 | $21,222 | $20,166 | $19,185 | $18,273 | $17,424 | $16,632 |
| 30 | $32,587 | $30,639 | $28,846 | $27,195 | $25,672 | $24,266 | $22,967 | $21,765 | $20,651 | $19,619 | $18,661 | $17,770 | $16,942 |
| 31 | $33,808 | $31,722 | $29,808 | $28,049 | $26,430 | $24,940 | $23,566 | $22,297 | $21,125 | $20,041 | $19,036 | $18,105 | $17,240 |
| 32 | $35,039 | $32,810 | $30,769 | $28,899 | $27,183 | $25,606 | $24,156 | $22,820 | $21,589 | $20,452 | $19,401 | $18,429 | $17,528 |
| 33 | $36,280 | $33,902 | $31,731 | $29,746 | $27,929 | $26,264 | $24,737 | $23,333 | $22,041 | $20,852 | $19,755 | $18,741 | $17,805 |
| 34 | $37,530 | $34,998 | $32,692 | $30,590 | $28,670 | $26,915 | $25,309 | $23,836 | $22,484 | $21,241 | $20,098 | $19,044 | $18,071 |
| 35 | $38,790 | $36,098 | $33,654 | $31,431 | $29,406 | $27,559 | $25,872 | $24,330 | $22,917 | $21,621 | $20,431 | $19,336 | $18,328 |
| 36 | $40,060 | $37,203 | $34,615 | $32,268 | $30,135 | $28,195 | $26,427 | $24,814 | $23,340 | $21,990 | $20,754 | $19,618 | $18,575 |
| 37 | $41,339 | $38,312 | $35,577 | $33,102 | $30,860 | $28,824 | $26,974 | $25,289 | $23,753 | $22,350 | $21,067 | $19,891 | $18,813 |
| 38 | $42,629 | $39,425 | $36,538 | $33,933 | $31,578 | $29,446 | $27,512 | $25,755 | $24,157 | $22,701 | $21,371 | $20,155 | $19,042 |
| 39 | $43,928 | $40,543 | $37,500 | $34,761 | $32,291 | $30,061 | $28,042 | $26,213 | $24,552 | $23,042 | $21,666 | $20,410 | $19,263 |
| 40 | $45,238 | $41,664 | $38,462 | $35,586 | $32,999 | $30,668 | $28,564 | $26,662 | $24,938 | $23,374 | $21,952 | $20,657 | $19,475 |
| 41 | $46,557 | $42,790 | $39,423 | $36,407 | $33,701 | $31,269 | $29,078 | $27,102 | $25,315 | $23,698 | $22,229 | $20,895 | $19,680 |
| 42 | $47,887 | $43,921 | $40,385 | $37,226 | $34,398 | $31,863 | $29,585 | $27,534 | $25,684 | $24,013 | $22,499 | $21,125 | $19,877 |
| 43 | $49,227 | $45,056 | $41,346 | $38,041 | $35,090 | $32,450 | $30,084 | $27,958 | $26,045 | $24,319 | $22,760 | $21,348 | $20,067 |
| 44 | $50,578 | $46,195 | $42,308 | $38,853 | $35,776 | $33,030 | $30,575 | $28,374 | $26,397 | $24,618 | $23,013 | $21,563 | $20,249 |
| 45 | $51,939 | $47,339 | $43,269 | $39,662 | $36,457 | $33,604 | $31,058 | $28,782 | $26,742 | $24,909 | $23,259 | $21,771 | $20,425 |
| 46 | $53,311 | $48,487 | $44,231 | $40,468 | $37,133 | $34,171 | $31,535 | $29,182 | $27,078 | $25,192 | $23,498 | $21,972 | $20,595 |

# CHART THREE

## STARTING PORTFOLIO NEEDED TO FUND VARIOUS ANNUAL EXPENSES
## ASSUMING NO TRUSTEE FEE AND 20% TAX RATE (CONTINUED)

**Inputs**

| | |
|---|---|
| R=real rate of return | 0.0% |
| T=tax rate | 20.0% |
| A=annual admin. fee | 0.0% |
| I=inflation | 4.0% |

| | 0.0% | 0.5% | 1.0% | 1.5% | 2.0% | 2.5% | 3.0% | 3.5% | 4.0% | 4.5% | 5.0% | 5.5% | 6.0% |
|---|---|---|---|---|---|---|---|---|---|---|---|---|---|
| | 1.032 | 1.036 | 1.04 | 1.044 | 1.048 | 1.052 | 1.056 | 1.06 | 1.064 | 1.068 | 1.072 | 1.076 | 1.08 |
| E=expenses to start (ann) | $1,000 | $1,000 | $1,000 | $1,000 | $1,000 | $1,000 | $1,000 | $1,000 | $1,000 | $1,000 | $1,000 | $1,000 | $1,000 |

Figures assume that expenses are all taken out at end of each year.

Rate of Return (Nominal):

| Life Expectancies | 4.0% | 4.5% | 5.0% | 5.5% | 6.0% | 6.5% | 7.0% | 7.5% | 8.0% | 8.5% | 9.0% | 9.5% | 10.0% |
|---|---|---|---|---|---|---|---|---|---|---|---|---|---|
| 47 | $54,693 | $49,639 | $45,192 | $41,271 | $37,804 | $34,732 | $32,004 | $29,575 | $27,407 | $25,468 | $23,729 | $22,166 | $20,758 |
| 48 | $56,086 | $50,796 | $46,154 | $42,070 | $38,470 | $35,287 | $32,466 | $29,960 | $27,729 | $25,737 | $23,954 | $22,354 | $20,915 |
| 49 | $57,490 | $51,957 | $47,115 | $42,867 | $39,130 | $35,835 | $32,921 | $30,339 | $28,043 | $25,998 | $24,172 | $22,535 | $21,066 |
| 50 | $58,904 | $53,123 | $48,077 | $43,661 | $39,786 | $36,377 | $33,369 | $30,709 | $28,351 | $26,253 | $24,383 | $22,711 | $21,212 |
| 51 | $60,330 | $54,294 | $49,038 | $44,451 | $40,436 | $36,912 | $33,811 | $31,073 | $28,651 | $26,501 | $24,588 | $22,880 | $21,352 |
| 52 | $61,767 | $55,468 | $50,000 | $45,239 | $41,082 | $37,442 | $34,245 | $31,431 | $28,945 | $26,743 | $24,787 | $23,044 | $21,487 |
| 53 | $63,214 | $56,648 | $50,962 | $46,023 | $41,722 | $37,965 | $34,673 | $31,781 | $29,232 | $26,978 | $24,980 | $23,203 | $21,617 |
| 54 | $64,674 | $57,832 | $51,923 | $46,805 | $42,358 | $38,483 | $35,095 | $32,125 | $29,512 | $27,207 | $25,167 | $23,356 | $21,743 |
| 55 | $66,144 | $59,020 | $52,885 | $47,583 | $42,989 | $38,994 | $35,510 | $32,462 | $29,786 | $27,430 | $25,348 | $23,504 | $21,863 |
| 56 | $67,626 | $60,214 | $53,846 | $48,359 | $43,615 | $39,500 | $35,919 | $32,793 | $30,054 | $27,647 | $25,525 | $23,647 | $21,980 |
| 57 | $69,119 | $61,411 | $54,808 | $49,131 | $44,236 | $40,000 | $36,322 | $33,118 | $30,316 | $27,859 | $25,695 | $23,785 | $22,091 |
| 58 | $70,624 | $62,614 | $55,769 | $49,901 | $44,853 | $40,494 | $36,719 | $33,436 | $30,572 | $28,065 | $25,861 | $23,918 | $22,199 |
| 59 | $72,140 | $63,821 | $56,731 | $50,668 | $45,464 | $40,983 | $37,109 | $33,749 | $30,822 | $28,265 | $26,022 | $24,048 | $22,303 |
| 60 | $73,668 | $65,032 | $57,692 | $51,431 | $46,072 | $41,466 | $37,494 | $34,055 | $31,067 | $28,460 | $26,178 | $24,172 | $22,403 |
| 61 | $75,208 | $66,249 | $58,654 | $52,192 | $46,674 | $41,944 | $37,873 | $34,356 | $31,306 | $28,651 | $26,330 | $24,293 | $22,499 |
| 62 | $76,760 | $67,470 | $59,615 | $52,950 | $47,272 | $42,416 | $38,246 | $34,651 | $31,540 | $28,836 | $26,476 | $24,410 | $22,592 |
| 63 | $78,324 | $68,695 | $60,577 | $53,705 | $47,865 | $42,882 | $38,613 | $34,941 | $31,768 | $29,016 | $26,619 | $24,522 | $22,681 |
| 64 | $79,901 | $69,926 | $61,538 | $54,457 | $48,454 | $43,344 | $38,975 | $35,225 | $31,992 | $29,192 | $26,757 | $24,631 | $22,767 |
| 65 | $81,489 | $71,161 | $62,500 | $55,206 | $49,038 | $43,800 | $39,332 | $35,504 | $32,210 | $29,363 | $26,891 | $24,736 | $22,849 |
| 66 | $83,090 | $72,401 | $63,462 | $55,953 | $49,618 | $44,251 | $39,683 | $35,777 | $32,423 | $29,529 | $27,021 | $24,838 | $22,929 |
| 67 | $84,703 | $73,646 | $64,423 | $56,696 | $50,194 | $44,697 | $40,029 | $36,046 | $32,632 | $29,691 | $27,148 | $24,937 | $23,006 |
| 68 | $86,328 | $74,896 | $65,385 | $57,437 | $50,765 | $45,138 | $40,369 | $36,309 | $32,835 | $29,849 | $27,270 | $25,032 | $23,080 |
| 69 | $87,967 | $76,150 | $66,346 | $58,175 | $51,331 | $45,573 | $40,704 | $36,567 | $33,035 | $30,003 | $27,389 | $25,123 | $23,151 |

THE LIFE PLANNING WORKBOOK

## Inputs

| | |
|---|---|
| R=real rate of return | 0.0% |
| T=tax rate | 20.0% |
| A=annual admin. fee | 0.0% |
| I=inflation | 4.0% |

| | 0.0% | 0.5% | 1.0% | 1.5% | 2.0% | 2.5% | 3.0% | 3.5% | 4.0% | 4.5% | 5.0% | 5.5% | 6.0% |
|---|---|---|---|---|---|---|---|---|---|---|---|---|---|
| | 1.032 | 1.036 | 1.04 | 1.044 | 1.048 | 1.052 | 1.056 | 1.06 | 1.064 | 1.068 | 1.072 | 1.076 | 1.08 |
| E=expenses to start (ann) | $1,000 | $1,000 | $1,000 | $1,000 | $1,000 | $1,000 | $1,000 | $1,000 | $1,000 | $1,000 | $1,000 | $1,000 | $1,000 |

Figures assume that expenses are all taken out at end of each year.

## Rate of Return (Nominal):

| Life Expectancies | 4.0% | 4.5% | 5.0% | 5.5% | 6.0% | 6.5% | 7.0% | 7.5% | 8.0% | 8.5% | 9.0% | 9.5% | 10.0% |
|---|---|---|---|---|---|---|---|---|---|---|---|---|---|
| 70 | $89,617 | $77,409 | $67,308 | $58,910 | $51,894 | $46,004 | $41,035 | $36,821 | $33,229 | $30,153 | $27,504 | $25,212 | $23,219 |
| 71 | $91,281 | $78,673 | $68,269 | $59,642 | $52,452 | $46,430 | $41,360 | $37,069 | $33,420 | $30,299 | $27,616 | $25,298 | $23,285 |
| 72 | $92,958 | $79,942 | $69,231 | $60,371 | $53,006 | $46,851 | $41,680 | $37,313 | $33,606 | $30,441 | $27,724 | $25,381 | $23,349 |
| 73 | $94,647 | $81,216 | $70,192 | $61,098 | $53,555 | $47,267 | $41,996 | $37,553 | $33,787 | $30,579 | $27,830 | $25,461 | $23,410 |
| 74 | $96,350 | $82,495 | $71,154 | $61,821 | $54,101 | $47,678 | $42,306 | $37,788 | $33,965 | $30,714 | $27,932 | $25,539 | $23,469 |
| 75 | $98,066 | $83,779 | $72,115 | $62,542 | $54,642 | $48,085 | $42,612 | $38,018 | $34,139 | $30,845 | $28,031 | $25,614 | $23,525 |
| 76 | $99,795 | $85,068 | $73,077 | $63,261 | $55,179 | $48,487 | $42,914 | $38,244 | $34,309 | $30,972 | $28,127 | $25,686 | $23,580 |
| 77 | $101,538 | $86,361 | $74,038 | $63,976 | $55,712 | $48,885 | $43,210 | $38,466 | $34,475 | $31,097 | $28,220 | $25,756 | $23,633 |
| 78 | $103,294 | $87,660 | $75,000 | $64,689 | $56,241 | $49,277 | $43,503 | $38,683 | $34,637 | $31,218 | $28,311 | $25,824 | $23,683 |
| 79 | $105,064 | $88,964 | $75,962 | $65,399 | $56,766 | $49,666 | $43,790 | $38,897 | $34,795 | $31,336 | $28,398 | $25,889 | $23,732 |
| 80 | $106,847 | $90,272 | $76,923 | $66,106 | $57,287 | $50,050 | $44,074 | $39,106 | $34,950 | $31,450 | $28,483 | $25,952 | $23,779 |
| 81 | $108,644 | $91,586 | $77,885 | $66,811 | $57,804 | $50,430 | $44,353 | $39,312 | $35,102 | $31,562 | $28,566 | $26,013 | $23,824 |
| 82 | $110,455 | $92,905 | $78,846 | $67,513 | $58,316 | $50,805 | $44,628 | $39,514 | $35,250 | $31,671 | $28,646 | $26,072 | $23,868 |
| 83 | $112,281 | $94,229 | $79,808 | $68,212 | $58,825 | $51,176 | $44,899 | $39,712 | $35,395 | $31,777 | $28,724 | $26,129 | $23,910 |
| 84 | $114,120 | $95,558 | $80,769 | $68,908 | $59,331 | $51,543 | $45,165 | $39,906 | $35,536 | $31,880 | $28,799 | $26,185 | $23,950 |
| 85 | $115,974 | $96,892 | $81,731 | $69,602 | $59,832 | $51,905 | $45,428 | $40,096 | $35,674 | $31,981 | $28,872 | $26,238 | $23,989 |
| 86 | $117,842 | $98,232 | $82,692 | $70,293 | $60,329 | $52,264 | $45,687 | $40,283 | $35,810 | $32,079 | $28,943 | $26,289 | $24,026 |
| 87 | $119,724 | $99,576 | $83,654 | $70,982 | $60,823 | $52,618 | $45,942 | $40,466 | $35,942 | $32,174 | $29,012 | $26,339 | $24,062 |
| 88 | $121,621 | $100,926 | $84,615 | $71,668 | $61,313 | $52,969 | $46,192 | $40,646 | $36,071 | $32,267 | $29,079 | $26,387 | $24,097 |
| 89 | $123,533 | $102,281 | $85,577 | $72,351 | $61,799 | $53,315 | $46,440 | $40,823 | $36,197 | $32,357 | $29,144 | $26,434 | $24,131 |
| 90 | $125,460 | $103,641 | $86,538 | $73,032 | $62,282 | $53,658 | $46,683 | $40,996 | $36,320 | $32,445 | $29,207 | $26,479 | $24,163 |

# STARTING PORTFOLIO NEEDED TO FUND VARIOUS ANNUAL EXPENSES ASSUMING NO TRUSTEE FEE AND 30% TAX RATE

**Inputs**

| | |
|---|---|
| R=real rate of return | 0.0% |
| T=tax rate | 30.0% |
| A=annual admin. fee | 0.0% |
| I=inflation | 4.0% |
| | 1.028 |
| E=expenses to start (ann) | $1,000 |

| 0.0% | 0.5% | 1.0% | 1.5% | 2.0% | 2.5% | 3.0% | 3.5% | 4.0% | 4.5% | 5.0% | 5.5% | 6.0% |
|---|---|---|---|---|---|---|---|---|---|---|---|---|
| 1.028 | 1.0315 | 1.035 | 1.0385 | 1.042 | 1.0455 | 1.049 | 1.0525 | 1.056 | 1.0595 | 1.063 | 1.0665 | 1.07 |
| $1,000 | $1,000 | $1,000 | $1,000 | $1,000 | $1,000 | $1,000 | $1,000 | $1,000 | $1,000 | $1,000 | $1,000 | $1,000 |

Figures assume that expenses are all taken out at end of each year.

**Rate of Return (Nominal):**

| Life Expectancies | 4.0% | 4.5% | 5.0% | 5.5% | 6.0% | 6.5% | 7.0% | 7.5% | 8.0% | 8.5% | 9.0% | 9.5% | 10.0% |
|---|---|---|---|---|---|---|---|---|---|---|---|---|---|
| 1 | $973 | $969 | $966 | $963 | $960 | $956 | $953 | $950 | $947 | $944 | $941 | $938 | $935 |
| 2 | $1,957 | $1,947 | $1,937 | $1,927 | $1,918 | $1,908 | $1,898 | $1,889 | $1,880 | $1,870 | $1,861 | $1,852 | $1,843 |
| 3 | $2,952 | $2,932 | $2,913 | $2,893 | $2,874 | $2,854 | $2,835 | $2,817 | $2,798 | $2,780 | $2,762 | $2,744 | $2,726 |
| 4 | $3,960 | $3,926 | $3,893 | $3,860 | $3,828 | $3,796 | $3,764 | $3,733 | $3,703 | $3,672 | $3,643 | $3,613 | $3,584 |
| 5 | $4,979 | $4,928 | $4,878 | $4,829 | $4,780 | $4,732 | $4,685 | $4,639 | $4,594 | $4,549 | $4,504 | $4,461 | $4,418 |
| 6 | $6,010 | $5,938 | $5,868 | $5,798 | $5,731 | $5,664 | $5,598 | $5,534 | $5,471 | $5,409 | $5,348 | $5,288 | $5,229 |
| 7 | $7,052 | $6,956 | $6,862 | $6,770 | $6,679 | $6,591 | $6,504 | $6,419 | $6,335 | $6,253 | $6,173 | $6,094 | $6,017 |
| 8 | $8,108 | $7,983 | $7,861 | $7,742 | $7,626 | $7,512 | $7,401 | $7,292 | $7,186 | $7,082 | $6,980 | $6,880 | $6,783 |
| 9 | $9,175 | $9,018 | $8,866 | $8,717 | $8,571 | $8,429 | $8,291 | $8,156 | $8,024 | $7,895 | $7,770 | $7,647 | $7,527 |
| 10 | $10,255 | $10,062 | $9,875 | $9,692 | $9,514 | $9,342 | $9,173 | $9,009 | $8,849 | $8,694 | $8,542 | $8,395 | $8,251 |
| 11 | $11,347 | $11,115 | $10,888 | $10,669 | $10,456 | $10,249 | $10,048 | $9,852 | $9,662 | $9,478 | $9,298 | $9,124 | $8,954 |
| 12 | $12,453 | $12,176 | $11,907 | $11,647 | $11,396 | $11,151 | $10,915 | $10,685 | $10,463 | $10,247 | $10,038 | $9,835 | $9,637 |
| 13 | $13,571 | $13,245 | $12,931 | $12,627 | $12,333 | $12,049 | $11,774 | $11,509 | $11,251 | $11,002 | $10,761 | $10,528 | $10,302 |
| 14 | $14,702 | $14,324 | $13,960 | $13,608 | $13,269 | $12,942 | $12,627 | $12,322 | $12,028 | $11,744 | $11,469 | $11,204 | $10,948 |
| 15 | $15,846 | $15,411 | $14,993 | $14,591 | $14,204 | $13,831 | $13,472 | $13,126 | $12,793 | $12,471 | $12,162 | $11,863 | $11,575 |
| 16 | $17,004 | $16,508 | $16,032 | $15,575 | $15,136 | $14,714 | $14,309 | $13,920 | $13,546 | $13,186 | $12,839 | $12,506 | $12,185 |
| 17 | $18,175 | $17,613 | $17,076 | $16,560 | $16,067 | $15,594 | $15,140 | $14,705 | $14,287 | $13,887 | $13,502 | $13,133 | $12,778 |
| 18 | $19,360 | $18,728 | $18,124 | $17,547 | $16,996 | $16,468 | $15,963 | $15,480 | $15,018 | $14,575 | $14,151 | $13,744 | $13,354 |
| 19 | $20,559 | $19,852 | $19,178 | $18,535 | $17,923 | $17,338 | $16,780 | $16,247 | $15,737 | $15,251 | $14,785 | $14,340 | $13,915 |
| 20 | $21,772 | $20,985 | $20,237 | $19,525 | $18,848 | $18,203 | $17,589 | $17,004 | $16,446 | $15,914 | $15,406 | $14,922 | $14,459 |
| 21 | $22,999 | $22,127 | $21,301 | $20,516 | $19,771 | $19,064 | $18,391 | $17,752 | $17,144 | $16,565 | $16,014 | $15,489 | $14,988 |
| 22 | $24,240 | $23,279 | $22,370 | $21,509 | $20,693 | $19,920 | $19,187 | $18,491 | $17,831 | $17,204 | $16,608 | $16,041 | $15,503 |
| 23 | $25,495 | $24,440 | $23,444 | $22,503 | $21,613 | $20,772 | $19,976 | $19,222 | $18,508 | $17,831 | $17,189 | $16,580 | $16,003 |

**Inputs**

| | |
|---|---|
| R=real rate of return | 0.0% |
| T=tax rate | 30.0% |
| A=annual admin. fee | 0.0% |
| I=inflation | 4.0% |

| | 0.0% | 0.5% | 1.0% | 1.5% | 2.0% | 2.5% | 3.0% | 3.5% | 4.0% | 4.5% | 5.0% | 5.5% | 6.0% |
|---|---|---|---|---|---|---|---|---|---|---|---|---|---|
| | 1.028 | 1.0315 | 1.035 | 1.0385 | 1.042 | 1.0455 | 1.049 | 1.0525 | 1.056 | 1.0595 | 1.063 | 1.0665 | 1.07 |
| E=expenses to start (ann) | $1,000 | $1,000 | $1,000 | $1,000 | $1,000 | $1,000 | $1,000 | $1,000 | $1,000 | $1,000 | $1,000 | $1,000 | $1,000 |

Figures assume that expenses are all taken out at end of each year.

| Rate of Return (Nominal): | 4.0% | 4.5% | 5.0% | 5.5% | 6.0% | 6.5% | 7.0% | 7.5% | 8.0% | 8.5% | 9.0% | 9.5% | 10.0% |
|---|---|---|---|---|---|---|---|---|---|---|---|---|---|
| **Life Expectancies** | | | | | | | | | | | | | |
| 24 | $26,766 | $25,611 | $24,523 | $23,498 | $22,531 | $21,619 | $20,757 | $19,944 | $19,174 | $18,447 | $17,758 | $17,106 | $16,488 |
| 25 | $28,051 | $26,792 | $25,608 | $24,495 | $23,448 | $22,462 | $21,533 | $20,657 | $19,831 | $19,051 | $18,315 | $17,619 | $16,961 |
| 26 | $29,351 | $27,982 | $26,698 | $25,493 | $24,362 | $23,300 | $22,301 | $21,362 | $20,477 | $19,644 | $18,859 | $18,119 | $17,420 |
| 27 | $30,667 | $29,182 | $27,793 | $26,493 | $25,275 | $24,134 | $23,063 | $22,058 | $21,114 | $20,226 | $19,392 | $18,606 | $17,866 |
| 28 | $31,997 | $30,392 | $28,894 | $27,494 | $26,187 | $24,963 | $23,819 | $22,746 | $21,741 | $20,798 | $19,913 | $19,081 | $18,300 |
| 29 | $33,344 | $31,612 | $29,999 | $28,497 | $27,096 | $25,789 | $24,567 | $23,426 | $22,359 | $21,359 | $20,423 | $19,545 | $18,721 |
| 30 | $34,706 | $32,842 | $31,111 | $29,501 | $28,004 | $26,609 | $25,310 | $24,098 | $22,967 | $21,910 | $20,922 | $19,997 | $19,131 |
| 31 | $36,084 | $34,082 | $32,227 | $30,507 | $28,910 | $27,426 | $26,046 | $24,762 | $23,566 | $22,450 | $21,410 | $20,438 | $19,529 |
| 32 | $37,478 | $35,332 | $33,349 | $31,514 | $29,814 | $28,238 | $26,776 | $25,418 | $24,156 | $22,981 | $21,887 | $20,867 | $19,916 |
| 33 | $38,888 | $36,593 | $34,476 | $32,522 | $30,716 | $29,046 | $27,500 | $26,066 | $24,737 | $23,502 | $22,354 | $21,287 | $20,292 |
| 34 | $40,314 | $37,864 | $35,609 | $33,532 | $31,617 | $29,850 | $28,217 | $26,707 | $25,309 | $24,013 | $22,811 | $21,695 | $20,658 |
| 35 | $41,758 | $39,145 | $36,747 | $34,543 | $32,516 | $30,649 | $28,928 | $27,340 | $25,872 | $24,515 | $23,259 | $22,094 | $21,013 |
| 36 | $43,218 | $40,437 | $37,891 | $35,556 | $33,413 | $31,444 | $29,633 | $27,965 | $26,427 | $25,008 | $23,696 | $22,483 | $21,359 |
| 37 | $44,695 | $41,740 | $39,040 | $36,570 | $34,309 | $32,235 | $30,332 | $28,583 | $26,974 | $25,491 | $24,124 | $22,862 | $21,694 |
| 38 | $46,190 | $43,053 | $40,195 | $37,586 | $35,203 | $33,022 | $31,025 | $29,194 | $27,512 | $25,966 | $24,543 | $23,231 | $22,021 |
| 39 | $47,702 | $44,378 | $41,355 | $38,603 | $36,095 | $33,805 | $31,712 | $29,797 | $28,042 | $26,432 | $24,953 | $23,592 | $22,338 |
| 40 | $49,231 | $45,713 | $42,521 | $39,622 | $36,985 | $34,584 | $32,394 | $30,393 | $28,564 | $26,889 | $25,353 | $23,943 | $22,646 |
| 41 | $50,779 | $47,059 | $43,693 | $40,642 | $37,874 | $35,358 | $33,069 | $30,983 | $29,078 | $27,338 | $25,746 | $24,286 | $22,946 |
| 42 | $52,344 | $48,416 | $44,870 | $41,664 | $38,761 | $36,129 | $33,739 | $31,565 | $29,585 | $27,779 | $26,129 | $24,620 | $23,237 |
| 43 | $53,928 | $49,785 | $46,053 | $42,687 | $39,646 | $36,895 | $34,402 | $32,140 | $30,084 | $28,212 | $26,505 | $24,946 | $23,520 |
| 44 | $55,530 | $51,164 | $47,242 | $43,712 | $40,530 | $37,658 | $35,060 | $32,708 | $30,575 | $28,636 | $26,872 | $25,264 | $23,795 |
| 45 | $57,151 | $52,555 | $48,436 | $44,738 | $41,412 | $38,416 | $35,713 | $33,270 | $31,058 | $29,053 | $27,231 | $25,574 | $24,063 |
| 46 | $58,791 | $53,958 | $49,636 | $45,765 | $42,292 | $39,170 | $36,360 | $33,825 | $31,535 | $29,462 | $27,583 | $25,876 | $24,323 |

# STARTING PORTFOLIO NEEDED TO FUND VARIOUS ANNUAL EXPENSES ASSUMING NO TRUSTEE FEE AND 30% TAX RATE (CONTINUED)

| Inputs | | |
|---|---|---|
| R=real rate of return | 0.0% | |
| T=tax rate | 30.0% | |
| A=annual admin. fee | 0.0% | |
| I=inflation | 4.0% | |
| E=expenses to start (ann) | 1.028 | $1,000 |

Figures assume that expenses are all taken out at end of each year.

| | 0.0% | 0.5% | 1.0% | 1.5% | 2.0% | 2.5% | 3.0% | 3.5% | 4.0% | 4.5% | 5.0% | 5.5% | 6.0% |
|---|---|---|---|---|---|---|---|---|---|---|---|---|---|
| | 1.028 | 1.0315 | 1.035 | 1.0385 | 1.042 | 1.0455 | 1.049 | 1.0525 | 1.056 | 1.0595 | 1.063 | 1.0665 | 1.07 |
| | $1,000 | $1,000 | $1,000 | $1,000 | $1,000 | $1,000 | $1,000 | $1,000 | $1,000 | $1,000 | $1,000 | $1,000 | $1,000 |

| Rate of Return (Nominal): | 4.0% | 4.5% | 5.0% | 5.5% | 6.0% | 6.5% | 7.0% | 7.5% | 8.0% | 8.5% | 9.0% | 9.5% | 10.0% |
|---|---|---|---|---|---|---|---|---|---|---|---|---|---|
| Life Expectancies | | | | | | | | | | | | | |
| 47 | $60,450 | $55,372 | $50,842 | $46,794 | $43,170 | $39,921 | $37,001 | $34,373 | $32,004 | $29,864 | $27,927 | $26,170 | $24,575 |
| 48 | $62,129 | $56,798 | $52,054 | $47,825 | $44,047 | $40,667 | $37,637 | $34,915 | $32,466 | $30,258 | $28,263 | $26,458 | $24,821 |
| 49 | $63,827 | $58,235 | $53,272 | $48,857 | $44,922 | $41,410 | $38,267 | $35,451 | $32,921 | $30,645 | $28,592 | $26,738 | $25,059 |
| 50 | $65,544 | $59,685 | $54,495 | $49,890 | $45,796 | $42,148 | $38,892 | $35,980 | $33,369 | $31,025 | $28,914 | $27,011 | $25,291 |
| 51 | $67,282 | $61,146 | $55,725 | $50,925 | $46,668 | $42,883 | $39,512 | $36,503 | $33,811 | $31,397 | $29,230 | $27,278 | $25,517 |
| 52 | $69,041 | $62,619 | $56,960 | $51,962 | $47,538 | $43,614 | $40,126 | $37,019 | $34,245 | $31,763 | $29,538 | $27,538 | $25,736 |
| 53 | $70,819 | $64,105 | $58,201 | $53,000 | $48,406 | $44,341 | $40,735 | $37,530 | $34,673 | $32,123 | $29,839 | $27,791 | $25,949 |
| 54 | $72,619 | $65,602 | $59,449 | $54,039 | $49,273 | $45,064 | $41,339 | $38,034 | $35,095 | $32,475 | $30,135 | $28,038 | $26,156 |
| 55 | $74,439 | $67,113 | $60,702 | $55,080 | $50,138 | $45,784 | $41,938 | $38,532 | $35,510 | $32,821 | $30,423 | $28,279 | $26,357 |
| 56 | $76,281 | $68,635 | $61,961 | $56,123 | $51,002 | $46,499 | $42,531 | $39,025 | $35,919 | $33,161 | $30,706 | $28,514 | $26,553 |
| 57 | $78,144 | $70,170 | $63,227 | $57,167 | $51,863 | $47,211 | $43,120 | $39,512 | $36,322 | $33,495 | $30,982 | $28,743 | $26,743 |
| 58 | $80,029 | $71,718 | $64,499 | $58,212 | $52,724 | $47,919 | $43,703 | $39,992 | $36,719 | $33,822 | $31,252 | $28,967 | $26,928 |
| 59 | $81,936 | $73,278 | $65,776 | $59,259 | $53,582 | $48,624 | $44,281 | $40,468 | $37,109 | $34,143 | $31,517 | $29,185 | $27,107 |
| 60 | $83,865 | $74,852 | $67,060 | $60,308 | $54,439 | $49,324 | $44,855 | $40,937 | $37,494 | $34,459 | $31,776 | $29,397 | $27,282 |
| 61 | $85,817 | $76,438 | $68,350 | $61,358 | $55,294 | $50,021 | $45,423 | $41,401 | $37,873 | $34,769 | $32,029 | $29,604 | $27,452 |
| 62 | $87,791 | $78,037 | $69,647 | $62,409 | $56,148 | $50,715 | $45,987 | $41,859 | $38,246 | $35,072 | $32,277 | $29,806 | $27,617 |
| 63 | $89,789 | $79,650 | $70,949 | $63,462 | $57,000 | $51,404 | $46,545 | $42,312 | $38,613 | $35,371 | $32,519 | $30,003 | $27,777 |
| 64 | $91,810 | $81,275 | $72,258 | $64,517 | $57,850 | $52,091 | $47,099 | $42,760 | $38,975 | $35,664 | $32,756 | $30,195 | $27,933 |
| 65 | $93,854 | $82,915 | $73,574 | $65,573 | $58,699 | $52,773 | $47,649 | $43,202 | $39,332 | $35,951 | $32,988 | $30,383 | $28,084 |
| 66 | $95,923 | $84,567 | $74,895 | $66,631 | $59,546 | $53,452 | $48,193 | $43,639 | $39,683 | $36,233 | $33,215 | $30,566 | $28,231 |
| 67 | $98,015 | $86,234 | $76,223 | $67,690 | $60,391 | $54,127 | $48,733 | $44,071 | $40,029 | $36,510 | $33,437 | $30,744 | $28,374 |
| 68 | $100,132 | $87,914 | $77,558 | $68,750 | $61,235 | $54,799 | $49,268 | $44,498 | $40,369 | $36,782 | $33,655 | $30,917 | $28,513 |
| 69 | $102,274 | $89,608 | $78,899 | $69,813 | $62,077 | $55,467 | $49,799 | $44,920 | $40,704 | $37,049 | $33,867 | $31,087 | $28,648 |

## Inputs

| | |
|---|---|
| R=real rate of return | 0.0% |
| T=tax rate | 30.0% |
| A=annual admin. fee | 0.0% |
| I=inflation | 4.0% |

| | 0.0% | 0.5% | 1.0% | 1.5% | 2.0% | 2.5% | 3.0% | 3.5% | 4.0% | 4.5% | 5.0% | 5.5% | 6.0% |
|---|---|---|---|---|---|---|---|---|---|---|---|---|---|
| | 1.028 | 1.0315 | 1.035 | 1.0385 | 1.042 | 1.0455 | 1.049 | 1.0525 | 1.056 | 1.0595 | 1.063 | 1.0665 | 1.07 |
| E=expenses to start (ann) | $1,000 | $1,000 | $1,000 | $1,000 | $1,000 | $1,000 | $1,000 | $1,000 | $1,000 | $1,000 | $1,000 | $1,000 | $1,000 |

Figures assume that expenses are all taken out at end of each year.

## Rate of Return (Nominal):

| Life Expectancies | 4.0% | 4.5% | 5.0% | 5.5% | 6.0% | 6.5% | 7.0% | 7.5% | 8.0% | 8.5% | 9.0% | 9.5% | 10.0% |
|---|---|---|---|---|---|---|---|---|---|---|---|---|---|
| 70 | $104,440 | $91,316 | $80,246 | $70,876 | $62,917 | $56,132 | $50,325 | $45,336 | $41,035 | $37,311 | $34,075 | $31,252 | $28,780 |
| 71 | $106,632 | $93,037 | $81,600 | $71,942 | $63,756 | $56,793 | $50,846 | $45,748 | $41,360 | $37,568 | $34,278 | $31,413 | $28,907 |
| 72 | $108,850 | $94,774 | $82,960 | $73,009 | $64,594 | $57,451 | $51,363 | $46,155 | $41,680 | $37,820 | $34,478 | $31,570 | $29,032 |
| 73 | $111,093 | $96,524 | $84,327 | $74,077 | $65,429 | $58,105 | $51,876 | $46,557 | $41,996 | $38,068 | $34,672 | $31,723 | $29,152 |
| 74 | $113,363 | $98,289 | $85,701 | $75,147 | $66,264 | $58,756 | $52,384 | $46,954 | $42,306 | $38,311 | $34,863 | $31,873 | $29,269 |
| 75 | $115,659 | $100,068 | $87,081 | $76,218 | $67,096 | $59,403 | $52,888 | $47,346 | $42,612 | $38,550 | $35,049 | $32,019 | $29,383 |
| 76 | $117,982 | $101,862 | $88,468 | $77,291 | $67,927 | $60,047 | $53,387 | $47,734 | $42,914 | $38,784 | $35,232 | $32,161 | $29,494 |
| 77 | $120,332 | $103,671 | $89,861 | $78,366 | $68,756 | $60,688 | $53,883 | $48,117 | $43,210 | $39,014 | $35,410 | $32,299 | $29,602 |
| 78 | $122,709 | $105,495 | $91,262 | $79,442 | $69,584 | $61,325 | $54,374 | $48,496 | $43,503 | $39,240 | $35,585 | $32,434 | $29,706 |
| 79 | $125,114 | $107,334 | $92,669 | $80,520 | $70,410 | $61,959 | $54,860 | $48,870 | $43,790 | $39,462 | $35,755 | $32,566 | $29,808 |
| 80 | $127,547 | $109,188 | $94,082 | $81,599 | $71,235 | $62,589 | $55,343 | $49,240 | $44,074 | $39,679 | $35,923 | $32,694 | $29,907 |
| 81 | $130,009 | $111,057 | $95,503 | $82,680 | $72,058 | $63,217 | $55,822 | $49,605 | $44,353 | $39,893 | $36,086 | $32,820 | $30,003 |
| 82 | $132,499 | $112,942 | $96,931 | $83,762 | $72,879 | $63,840 | $56,296 | $49,966 | $44,628 | $40,103 | $36,246 | $32,942 | $30,096 |
| 83 | $135,019 | $114,842 | $98,365 | $84,846 | $73,699 | $64,461 | $56,766 | $50,323 | $44,899 | $40,308 | $36,402 | $33,061 | $30,187 |
| 84 | $137,568 | $116,758 | $99,807 | $85,932 | $74,517 | $65,078 | $57,232 | $50,675 | $45,165 | $40,510 | $36,556 | $33,177 | $30,275 |
| 85 | $140,146 | $118,689 | $101,255 | $87,019 | $75,334 | $65,693 | $57,695 | $51,024 | $45,428 | $40,709 | $36,705 | $33,290 | $30,361 |
| 86 | $142,755 | $120,637 | $102,710 | $88,107 | $76,149 | $66,303 | $58,153 | $51,368 | $45,687 | $40,903 | $36,852 | $33,401 | $30,444 |
| 87 | $145,394 | $122,600 | $104,173 | $89,197 | $76,962 | $66,911 | $58,607 | $51,708 | $45,942 | $41,094 | $36,995 | $33,509 | $30,525 |
| 88 | $148,064 | $124,580 | $105,642 | $90,289 | $77,774 | $67,516 | $59,058 | $52,044 | $46,192 | $41,282 | $37,135 | $33,614 | $30,604 |
| 89 | $150,765 | $126,576 | $107,119 | $91,382 | $78,585 | $68,117 | $59,504 | $52,376 | $46,440 | $41,466 | $37,273 | $33,716 | $30,681 |
| 90 | $153,498 | $128,588 | $108,602 | $92,477 | $79,394 | $68,715 | $59,947 | $52,704 | $46,683 | $41,646 | $37,407 | $33,816 | $30,755 |

# CHART FIVE

## STARTING PORTFOLIO NEEDED TO FUND VARIOUS ANNUAL EXPENSES
### ASSUMING 1% TRUSTEE FEE AND 0% TAX RATE

**Inputs**

| | |
|---|---|
| R=real rate of return | 0.0% |
| T=tax rate | 0.0% |
| A=annual admin. fee | 1.0% |
| I=inflation | 4.0% |

| | 0.0% | 0.5% | 1.0% | 1.5% | 2.0% | 2.5% | 3.0% | 3.5% | 4.0% | 4.5% | 5.0% | 5.5% | 6.0% |
|---|---|---|---|---|---|---|---|---|---|---|---|---|---|
| E=expenses to start (ann) | 1.03 | 1.035 | 1.04 | 1.045 | 1.05 | 1.055 | 1.06 | 1.065 | 1.07 | 1.075 | 1.08 | 1.085 | 1.09 |
| | $1,000 | $1,000 | $1,000 | $1,000 | $1,000 | $1,000 | $1,000 | $1,000 | $1,000 | $1,000 | $1,000 | $1,000 | $1,000 |

Figures assume that expenses are all taken out at end of each year.

**Rate of Return (Nominal):**

| Life Expectancies | 4.0% | 4.5% | 5.0% | 5.5% | 6.0% | 6.5% | 7.0% | 7.5% | 8.0% | 8.5% | 9.0% | 9.5% | 10.0% |
|---|---|---|---|---|---|---|---|---|---|---|---|---|---|
| 1 | $971 | $966 | $962 | $957 | $952 | $948 | $943 | $939 | $935 | $930 | $926 | $922 | $917 |
| 2 | $1,951 | $1,937 | $1,923 | $1,909 | $1,896 | $1,882 | $1,869 | $1,856 | $1,843 | $1,830 | $1,818 | $1,805 | $1,793 |
| 3 | $2,941 | $2,913 | $2,885 | $2,857 | $2,830 | $2,803 | $2,777 | $2,751 | $2,726 | $2,701 | $2,676 | $2,652 | $2,628 |
| 4 | $3,940 | $3,893 | $3,846 | $3,800 | $3,755 | $3,711 | $3,668 | $3,626 | $3,584 | $3,543 | $3,503 | $3,464 | $3,425 |
| 5 | $4,950 | $4,878 | $4,808 | $4,739 | $4,672 | $4,606 | $4,542 | $4,480 | $4,418 | $4,358 | $4,299 | $4,242 | $4,185 |
| 6 | $5,968 | $5,868 | $5,769 | $5,673 | $5,580 | $5,489 | $5,400 | $5,313 | $5,229 | $5,146 | $5,066 | $4,987 | $4,911 |
| 7 | $6,997 | $6,862 | $6,731 | $6,603 | $6,479 | $6,359 | $6,242 | $6,128 | $6,017 | $5,909 | $5,804 | $5,702 | $5,603 |
| 8 | $8,036 | $7,861 | $7,692 | $7,529 | $7,370 | $7,216 | $7,067 | $6,923 | $6,783 | $6,647 | $6,515 | $6,387 | $6,263 |
| 9 | $9,085 | $8,866 | $8,654 | $8,449 | $8,252 | $8,061 | $7,877 | $7,699 | $7,527 | $7,361 | $7,200 | $7,044 | $6,893 |
| 10 | $10,144 | $9,875 | $9,615 | $9,366 | $9,126 | $8,895 | $8,672 | $8,457 | $8,251 | $8,051 | $7,859 | $7,674 | $7,495 |
| 11 | $11,213 | $10,888 | $10,577 | $10,278 | $9,991 | $9,716 | $9,452 | $9,198 | $8,954 | $8,719 | $8,494 | $8,277 | $8,068 |
| 12 | $12,293 | $11,907 | $11,538 | $11,186 | $10,849 | $10,526 | $10,217 | $9,921 | $9,637 | $9,366 | $9,105 | $8,855 | $8,616 |
| 13 | $13,383 | $12,931 | $12,500 | $12,089 | $11,698 | $11,324 | $10,967 | $10,627 | $10,302 | $9,991 | $9,694 | $9,410 | $9,138 |
| 14 | $14,484 | $13,960 | $13,462 | $12,988 | $12,539 | $12,111 | $11,704 | $11,316 | $10,948 | $10,596 | $10,261 | $9,941 | $9,636 |
| 15 | $15,596 | $14,993 | $14,423 | $13,883 | $13,372 | $12,887 | $12,426 | $11,990 | $11,575 | $11,181 | $10,807 | $10,450 | $10,111 |
| 16 | $16,718 | $16,032 | $15,385 | $14,774 | $14,197 | $13,651 | $13,135 | $12,647 | $12,185 | $11,747 | $11,332 | $10,939 | $10,565 |
| 17 | $17,851 | $17,076 | $16,346 | $15,660 | $15,014 | $14,405 | $13,831 | $13,289 | $12,778 | $12,295 | $11,839 | $11,407 | $10,998 |
| 18 | $18,995 | $18,124 | $17,308 | $16,542 | $15,823 | $15,148 | $14,513 | $13,916 | $13,354 | $12,825 | $12,326 | $11,855 | $11,411 |
| 19 | $20,151 | $19,178 | $18,269 | $17,420 | $16,625 | $15,880 | $15,183 | $14,529 | $13,915 | $13,338 | $12,795 | $12,285 | $11,805 |
| 20 | $21,317 | $20,237 | $19,231 | $18,293 | $17,419 | $16,603 | $15,840 | $15,127 | $14,459 | $13,834 | $13,247 | $12,697 | $12,181 |
| 21 | $22,495 | $21,301 | $20,192 | $19,163 | $18,205 | $17,314 | $16,484 | $15,711 | $14,988 | $14,314 | $13,683 | $13,092 | $12,539 |
| 22 | $23,684 | $22,370 | $21,154 | $20,028 | $18,984 | $18,016 | $17,117 | $16,281 | $15,503 | $14,778 | $14,102 | $13,471 | $12,882 |
| 23 | $24,885 | $23,444 | $22,115 | $20,889 | $19,756 | $18,708 | $17,737 | $16,837 | $16,003 | $15,227 | $14,506 | $13,834 | $13,208 |

THE LIFE PLANNING WORKBOOK

**Inputs**

| | |
|---|---|
| R=real rate of return | 0.0% |
| T=tax rate | 0.0% |
| A=annual admin. fee | 1.0% |
| I=inflation | 4.0% |

| 6.0% | 5.5% | 5.0% | 4.5% | 4.0% | 3.5% | 3.0% | 2.5% | 2.0% | 1.5% | 1.0% | 0.5% | 0.0% |
|---|---|---|---|---|---|---|---|---|---|---|---|---|
| 1.09 | 1.085 | 1.08 | 1.075 | 1.07 | 1.065 | 1.06 | 1.055 | 1.05 | 1.045 | 1.04 | 1.035 | 1.03 |
| $1,000 | $1,000 | $1,000 | $1,000 | $1,000 | $1,000 | $1,000 | $1,000 | $1,000 | $1,000 | $1,000 | $1,000 | $1,000 |

E=expenses to start (ann)

Figures assume that expenses are all taken out at end of each year.

**Rate of Return (Nominal):**

| Life Expectancies | 4.0% | 4.5% | 5.0% | 5.5% | 6.0% | 6.5% | 7.0% | 7.5% | 8.0% | 8.5% | 9.0% | 9.5% | 10.0% |
|---|---|---|---|---|---|---|---|---|---|---|---|---|---|
| 24 | $26,098 | $24,523 | $23,077 | $21,746 | $20,520 | $19,390 | $18,346 | $17,381 | $16,488 | $15,661 | $14,894 | $14,182 | $13,520 |
| 25 | $27,322 | $25,608 | $24,038 | $22,599 | $21,277 | $20,062 | $18,943 | $17,912 | $16,961 | $16,082 | $15,269 | $14,515 | $13,817 |
| 26 | $28,558 | $26,698 | $25,000 | $23,448 | $22,027 | $20,724 | $19,529 | $18,431 | $17,420 | $16,488 | $15,629 | $14,835 | $14,101 |
| 27 | $29,806 | $27,793 | $25,962 | $24,292 | $22,769 | $21,378 | $20,104 | $18,937 | $17,866 | $16,882 | $15,976 | $15,141 | $14,371 |
| 28 | $31,066 | $28,894 | $26,923 | $25,133 | $23,505 | $22,022 | $20,668 | $19,431 | $18,300 | $17,262 | $16,310 | $15,435 | $14,629 |
| 29 | $32,339 | $29,999 | $27,885 | $25,970 | $24,234 | $22,656 | $21,222 | $19,914 | $18,721 | $17,631 | $16,632 | $15,717 | $14,876 |
| 30 | $33,624 | $31,111 | $28,846 | $26,803 | $24,955 | $23,282 | $21,765 | $20,386 | $19,131 | $17,987 | $16,942 | $15,986 | $15,111 |
| 31 | $34,921 | $32,227 | $29,808 | $27,631 | $25,670 | $23,899 | $22,297 | $20,846 | $19,529 | $18,331 | $17,240 | $16,245 | $15,335 |
| 32 | $36,231 | $33,349 | $30,769 | $28,456 | $26,378 | $24,507 | $22,820 | $21,296 | $19,916 | $18,665 | $17,528 | $16,493 | $15,549 |
| 33 | $37,554 | $34,476 | $31,731 | $29,277 | $27,079 | $25,106 | $23,333 | $21,735 | $20,292 | $18,987 | $17,805 | $16,731 | $15,753 |
| 34 | $38,889 | $35,609 | $32,692 | $30,094 | $27,773 | $25,697 | $23,836 | $22,164 | $20,658 | $19,299 | $18,071 | $16,958 | $15,948 |
| 35 | $40,237 | $36,747 | $33,654 | $30,907 | $28,461 | $26,280 | $24,330 | $22,582 | $21,013 | $19,601 | $18,328 | $17,177 | $16,134 |
| 36 | $41,599 | $37,891 | $34,615 | $31,716 | $29,143 | $26,854 | $24,814 | $22,991 | $21,359 | $19,893 | $18,575 | $17,386 | $16,311 |
| 37 | $42,974 | $39,040 | $35,577 | $32,521 | $29,817 | $27,420 | $25,289 | $23,390 | $21,694 | $20,176 | $18,813 | $17,586 | $16,480 |
| 38 | $44,362 | $40,195 | $36,538 | $33,322 | $30,486 | $27,978 | $25,755 | $23,780 | $22,021 | $20,449 | $19,042 | $17,779 | $16,642 |
| 39 | $45,763 | $41,355 | $37,500 | $34,120 | $31,148 | $28,528 | $26,213 | $24,161 | $22,338 | $20,714 | $19,263 | $17,963 | $16,796 |
| 40 | $47,179 | $42,521 | $38,462 | $34,913 | $31,804 | $29,070 | $26,662 | $24,533 | $22,646 | $20,969 | $19,475 | $18,140 | $16,943 |
| 41 | $48,607 | $43,693 | $39,423 | $35,703 | $32,453 | $29,605 | $27,102 | $24,896 | $22,946 | $21,217 | $19,680 | $18,309 | $17,083 |
| 42 | $50,050 | $44,870 | $40,385 | $36,489 | $33,096 | $30,132 | $27,534 | $25,251 | $23,237 | $21,456 | $19,877 | $18,471 | $17,217 |
| 43 | $51,507 | $46,053 | $41,346 | $37,272 | $33,734 | $30,651 | $27,958 | $25,597 | $23,520 | $21,688 | $20,067 | $18,627 | $17,345 |
| 44 | $52,978 | $47,242 | $42,308 | $38,050 | $34,365 | $31,163 | $28,374 | $25,935 | $23,795 | $21,912 | $20,249 | $18,776 | $17,466 |
| 45 | $54,463 | $48,436 | $43,269 | $38,825 | $34,990 | $31,668 | $28,782 | $26,265 | $24,063 | $22,129 | $20,425 | $18,919 | $17,583 |
| 46 | $55,963 | $49,636 | $44,231 | $39,596 | $35,609 | $32,166 | $29,182 | $26,587 | $24,323 | $22,339 | $20,595 | $19,056 | $17,694 |

## STARTING PORTFOLIO NEEDED TO FUND VARIOUS ANNUAL EXPENSES
## ASSUMING 1% TRUSTEE FEE AND 0% TAX RATE (CONTINUED)

### Inputs

| | |
|---|---|
| R=real rate of return | 0.0% |
| T=tax rate | 0.0% |
| A=annual admin. fee | 1.0% |
| I=inflation | 4.0% |
| | 1.03 |
| E=expenses to start (ann) | $1,000 |

| 0.5% | 1.0% | 1.5% | 2.0% | 2.5% | 3.0% | 3.5% | 4.0% | 4.5% | 5.0% | 5.5% | 6.0% |
|---|---|---|---|---|---|---|---|---|---|---|---|
| 1.035 | 1.04 | 1.045 | 1.05 | 1.055 | 1.06 | 1.065 | 1.07 | 1.075 | 1.08 | 1.085 | 1.09 |
| $1,000 | $1,000 | $1,000 | $1,000 | $1,000 | $1,000 | $1,000 | $1,000 | $1,000 | $1,000 | $1,000 | $1,000 |

Figures assume that expenses are all taken out at end of each year.

### Rate of Return (Nominal):

| Life Expectancies | 4.0% | 4.5% | 5.0% | 5.5% | 6.0% | 6.5% | 7.0% | 7.5% | 8.0% | 8.5% | 9.0% | 9.5% | 10.0% |
|---|---|---|---|---|---|---|---|---|---|---|---|---|---|
| 47 | $57,477 | $50,842 | $45,192 | $40,364 | $36,222 | $32,656 | $29,575 | $26,902 | $24,575 | $22,542 | $20,758 | $19,187 | $17,799 |
| 48 | $59,006 | $52,054 | $46,154 | $41,128 | $36,830 | $33,140 | $29,960 | $27,210 | $24,821 | $22,738 | $20,915 | $19,313 | $17,900 |
| 49 | $60,550 | $53,272 | $47,115 | $41,888 | $37,431 | $33,617 | $30,339 | $27,510 | $25,059 | $22,928 | $21,066 | $19,434 | $17,997 |
| 50 | $62,108 | $54,495 | $48,077 | $42,644 | $38,027 | $34,087 | $30,709 | $27,803 | $25,291 | $23,112 | $21,212 | $19,549 | $18,089 |
| 51 | $63,682 | $55,725 | $49,038 | $43,397 | $38,617 | $34,550 | $31,073 | $28,089 | $25,517 | $23,289 | $21,352 | $19,660 | $18,176 |
| 52 | $65,271 | $56,960 | $50,000 | $44,147 | $39,202 | $35,006 | $31,431 | $28,369 | $25,736 | $23,461 | $21,487 | $19,767 | $18,260 |
| 53 | $66,876 | $58,201 | $50,962 | $44,892 | $39,781 | $35,457 | $31,781 | $28,642 | $25,949 | $23,628 | $21,617 | $19,868 | $18,340 |
| 54 | $68,496 | $59,449 | $51,923 | $45,634 | $40,354 | $35,900 | $32,125 | $28,909 | $26,156 | $23,789 | $21,743 | $19,966 | $18,416 |
| 55 | $70,132 | $60,702 | $52,885 | $46,373 | $40,922 | $36,338 | $32,462 | $29,169 | $26,357 | $23,944 | $21,863 | $20,060 | $18,489 |
| 56 | $71,784 | $61,961 | $53,846 | $47,108 | $41,485 | $36,769 | $32,793 | $29,423 | $26,553 | $24,095 | $21,980 | $20,149 | $18,558 |
| 57 | $73,452 | $63,227 | $54,808 | $47,840 | $42,042 | $37,194 | $33,118 | $29,672 | $26,743 | $24,241 | $22,091 | $20,235 | $18,624 |
| 58 | $75,136 | $64,499 | $55,769 | $48,568 | $42,594 | $37,613 | $33,436 | $29,914 | $26,928 | $24,382 | $22,199 | $20,318 | $18,687 |
| 59 | $76,836 | $65,776 | $56,731 | $49,292 | $43,141 | $38,026 | $33,749 | $30,151 | $27,107 | $24,518 | $22,303 | $20,397 | $18,747 |
| 60 | $78,553 | $67,060 | $57,692 | $50,013 | $43,683 | $38,433 | $34,055 | $30,382 | $27,282 | $24,650 | $22,403 | $20,472 | $18,805 |
| 61 | $80,286 | $68,350 | $58,654 | $50,731 | $44,219 | $38,835 | $34,356 | $30,608 | $27,452 | $24,778 | $22,499 | $20,545 | $18,860 |
| 62 | $82,037 | $69,647 | $59,615 | $51,445 | $44,750 | $39,231 | $34,651 | $30,828 | $27,617 | $24,901 | $22,592 | $20,615 | $18,912 |
| 63 | $83,804 | $70,949 | $60,577 | $52,156 | $45,276 | $39,621 | $34,941 | $31,044 | $27,777 | $25,021 | $22,681 | $20,681 | $18,962 |
| 64 | $85,589 | $72,258 | $61,538 | $52,863 | $45,798 | $40,005 | $35,225 | $31,254 | $27,933 | $25,136 | $22,767 | $20,745 | $19,009 |
| 65 | $87,390 | $73,574 | $62,500 | $53,567 | $46,314 | $40,384 | $35,504 | $31,459 | $28,084 | $25,248 | $22,849 | $20,806 | $19,055 |
| 66 | $89,210 | $74,895 | $63,462 | $54,268 | $46,825 | $40,758 | $35,777 | $31,660 | $28,231 | $25,356 | $22,929 | $20,865 | $19,098 |
| 67 | $91,047 | $76,223 | $64,423 | $54,965 | $47,332 | $41,126 | $36,046 | $31,855 | $28,374 | $25,461 | $23,006 | $20,921 | $19,140 |
| 68 | $92,902 | $77,558 | $65,385 | $55,659 | $47,833 | $41,489 | $36,309 | $32,047 | $28,513 | $25,562 | $23,080 | $20,975 | $19,179 |
| 69 | $94,774 | $78,899 | $66,346 | $56,350 | $48,330 | $41,847 | $36,567 | $32,233 | $28,648 | $25,660 | $23,151 | $21,027 | $19,217 |

## Inputs

| | | | | | | | | | | | | | |
|---|---|---|---|---|---|---|---|---|---|---|---|---|---|
| R=real rate of return | 0.0% | | | | | | | | | | | | |
| T=tax rate | 0.0% | | | | | | | | | | | | |
| A=annual admin. fee | 1.0% | | | | | | | | | | | | |
| I=inflation | 4.0% | | | | | | | | | | | | |
| | 0.0% | 0.5% | 1.0% | 1.5% | 2.0% | 2.5% | 3.0% | 3.5% | 4.0% | 4.5% | 5.0% | 5.5% | 6.0% |
| | 1.03 | 1.035 | 1.04 | 1.045 | 1.05 | 1.055 | 1.06 | 1.065 | 1.07 | 1.075 | 1.08 | 1.085 | 1.09 |
| E=expenses to start (ann) | $1,000 | $1,000 | $1,000 | $1,000 | $1,000 | $1,000 | $1,000 | $1,000 | $1,000 | $1,000 | $1,000 | $1,000 | $1,000 |

Figures assume that expenses are all taken out at end of each year.

## Rate of Return (Nominal):

| Life Expectancies | 4.0% | 4.5% | 5.0% | 5.5% | 6.0% | 6.5% | 7.0% | 7.5% | 8.0% | 8.5% | 9.0% | 9.5% | 10.0% |
|---|---|---|---|---|---|---|---|---|---|---|---|---|---|
| 70 | $96,665 | $80,246 | $67,308 | $57,037 | $48,822 | $42,200 | $36,821 | $32,416 | $28,780 | $25,755 | $23,219 | $21,077 | $19,253 |
| 71 | $98,575 | $81,600 | $68,269 | $57,721 | $49,309 | $42,548 | $37,069 | $32,594 | $28,907 | $25,847 | $23,285 | $21,124 | $19,287 |
| 72 | $100,503 | $82,960 | $69,231 | $58,402 | $49,792 | $42,891 | $37,313 | $32,767 | $29,032 | $25,936 | $23,349 | $21,170 | $19,320 |
| 73 | $102,449 | $84,327 | $70,192 | $59,079 | $50,270 | $43,229 | $37,553 | $32,937 | $29,152 | $26,021 | $23,410 | $21,213 | $19,351 |
| 74 | $104,415 | $85,701 | $71,154 | $59,754 | $50,744 | $43,562 | $37,788 | $33,103 | $29,269 | $26,104 | $23,469 | $21,255 | $19,381 |
| 75 | $106,399 | $87,081 | $72,115 | $60,425 | $51,213 | $43,891 | $38,018 | $33,265 | $29,383 | $26,185 | $23,525 | $21,295 | $19,409 |
| 76 | $108,403 | $88,468 | $73,077 | $61,092 | $51,678 | $44,215 | $38,244 | $33,423 | $29,494 | $26,262 | $23,580 | $21,334 | $19,436 |
| 77 | $110,427 | $89,861 | $74,038 | $61,757 | $52,138 | $44,534 | $38,466 | $33,577 | $29,602 | $26,338 | $23,633 | $21,371 | $19,462 |
| 78 | $112,470 | $91,262 | $75,000 | $62,419 | $52,594 | $44,849 | $38,683 | $33,728 | $29,706 | $26,410 | $23,683 | $21,406 | $19,487 |
| 79 | $114,532 | $92,669 | $75,962 | $63,077 | $53,045 | $45,159 | $38,897 | $33,875 | $29,808 | $26,481 | $23,732 | $21,440 | $19,510 |
| 80 | $116,615 | $94,082 | $76,923 | $63,732 | $53,492 | $45,465 | $39,106 | $34,019 | $29,907 | $26,549 | $23,779 | $21,472 | $19,533 |
| 81 | $118,718 | $95,503 | $77,885 | $64,384 | $53,935 | $45,766 | $39,312 | $34,160 | $30,003 | $26,615 | $23,824 | $21,503 | $19,554 |
| 82 | $120,842 | $96,931 | $78,846 | $65,033 | $54,374 | $46,063 | $39,514 | $34,297 | $30,096 | $26,678 | $23,868 | $21,533 | $19,575 |
| 83 | $122,986 | $98,365 | $79,808 | $65,679 | $54,809 | $46,356 | $39,712 | $34,431 | $30,187 | $26,740 | $23,910 | $21,562 | $19,594 |
| 84 | $125,151 | $99,807 | $80,769 | $66,321 | $55,239 | $46,645 | $39,906 | $34,561 | $30,275 | $26,800 | $23,950 | $21,589 | $19,613 |
| 85 | $127,337 | $101,255 | $81,731 | $66,961 | $55,665 | $46,930 | $40,096 | $34,689 | $30,361 | $26,857 | $23,989 | $21,615 | $19,631 |
| 86 | $129,544 | $102,710 | $82,692 | $67,597 | $56,088 | $47,210 | $40,283 | $34,814 | $30,444 | $26,913 | $24,026 | $21,641 | $19,647 |
| 87 | $131,773 | $104,173 | $83,654 | $68,231 | $56,506 | $47,487 | $40,466 | $34,935 | $30,525 | $26,967 | $24,062 | $21,665 | $19,664 |
| 88 | $134,023 | $105,642 | $84,615 | $68,861 | $56,920 | $47,760 | $40,646 | $35,054 | $30,604 | $27,019 | $24,097 | $21,688 | $19,679 |
| 89 | $136,295 | $107,119 | $85,577 | $69,489 | $57,330 | $48,028 | $40,823 | $35,170 | $30,681 | $27,070 | $24,131 | $21,710 | $19,694 |
| 90 | $138,589 | $108,602 | $86,538 | $70,113 | $57,737 | $48,293 | $40,996 | $35,284 | $30,755 | $27,119 | $24,163 | $21,731 | $19,708 |

# Chart Six

## Starting Portfolio Needed to Fund Various Annual Expenses Assuming 1% Trustee Fee and 10% Tax Rate

**Inputs**

| | |
|---|---|
| R=real rate of return | 0.0% |
| T=tax rate | 10.0% |
| A=annual admin. fee | 1.0% |
| I=inflation | 4.0% |

| | 0.0% | 0.5% | 1.0% | 1.5% | 2.0% | 2.5% | 3.0% | 3.5% | 4.0% | 4.5% | 5.0% | 5.5% | 6.0% |
|---|---|---|---|---|---|---|---|---|---|---|---|---|---|
| | 1.026 | 1.0305 | 1.035 | 1.0395 | 1.044 | 1.0485 | 1.053 | 1.0575 | 1.062 | 1.0665 | 1.071 | 1.0755 | 1.08 |
| E=expenses to start (ann) | $1,000 | $1,000 | $1,000 | $1,000 | $1,000 | $1,000 | $1,000 | $1,000 | $1,000 | $1,000 | $1,000 | $1,000 | $1,000 |

Figures assume that expenses are all taken out at end of each year.

| Rate of Return (Nominal): | 4.0% | 4.5% | 5.0% | 5.5% | 6.0% | 6.5% | 7.0% | 7.5% | 8.0% | 8.5% | 9.0% | 9.5% | 10.0% |
|---|---|---|---|---|---|---|---|---|---|---|---|---|---|
| Life Expectancies | | | | | | | | | | | | | |
| 1 | $975 | $970 | $966 | $962 | $958 | $954 | $950 | $946 | $942 | $938 | $934 | $930 | $926 |
| 2 | $1,963 | $1,950 | $1,937 | $1,924 | $1,912 | $1,900 | $1,888 | $1,876 | $1,864 | $1,852 | $1,840 | $1,829 | $1,818 |
| 3 | $2,964 | $2,938 | $2,913 | $2,887 | $2,863 | $2,838 | $2,814 | $2,790 | $2,767 | $2,744 | $2,721 | $2,698 | $2,676 |
| 4 | $3,979 | $3,936 | $3,893 | $3,851 | $3,809 | $3,769 | $3,729 | $3,690 | $3,651 | $3,613 | $3,576 | $3,539 | $3,503 |
| 5 | $5,008 | $4,942 | $4,878 | $4,815 | $4,753 | $4,692 | $4,633 | $4,574 | $4,517 | $4,461 | $4,406 | $4,352 | $4,299 |
| 6 | $6,051 | $5,958 | $5,868 | $5,779 | $5,692 | $5,608 | $5,525 | $5,444 | $5,365 | $5,288 | $5,212 | $5,138 | $5,066 |
| 7 | $7,108 | $6,984 | $6,862 | $6,744 | $6,628 | $6,516 | $6,406 | $6,300 | $6,196 | $6,094 | $5,995 | $5,898 | $5,804 |
| 8 | $8,180 | $8,018 | $7,861 | $7,709 | $7,561 | $7,417 | $7,277 | $7,141 | $7,009 | $6,880 | $6,755 | $6,634 | $6,515 |
| 9 | $9,266 | $9,063 | $8,866 | $8,675 | $8,490 | $8,311 | $8,137 | $7,969 | $7,805 | $7,647 | $7,493 | $7,344 | $7,200 |
| 10 | $10,367 | $10,117 | $9,875 | $9,641 | $9,415 | $9,197 | $8,986 | $8,782 | $8,585 | $8,395 | $8,210 | $8,032 | $7,859 |
| 11 | $11,483 | $11,180 | $10,888 | $10,607 | $10,337 | $10,076 | $9,825 | $9,583 | $9,349 | $9,124 | $8,906 | $8,696 | $8,494 |
| 12 | $12,615 | $12,254 | $11,907 | $11,575 | $11,255 | $10,948 | $10,653 | $10,370 | $10,097 | $9,835 | $9,582 | $9,339 | $9,105 |
| 13 | $13,762 | $13,337 | $12,931 | $12,542 | $12,170 | $11,813 | $11,471 | $11,144 | $10,829 | $10,528 | $10,239 | $9,961 | $9,694 |
| 14 | $14,924 | $14,431 | $13,960 | $13,510 | $13,081 | $12,671 | $12,279 | $11,905 | $11,547 | $11,204 | $10,876 | $10,562 | $10,261 |
| 15 | $16,102 | $15,534 | $14,993 | $14,479 | $13,989 | $13,522 | $13,077 | $12,653 | $12,249 | $11,863 | $11,495 | $11,143 | $10,807 |
| 16 | $17,297 | $16,648 | $16,032 | $15,448 | $14,893 | $14,366 | $13,866 | $13,390 | $12,937 | $12,506 | $12,096 | $11,705 | $11,332 |
| 17 | $18,507 | $17,771 | $17,076 | $16,417 | $15,794 | $15,204 | $14,644 | $14,114 | $13,611 | $13,133 | $12,679 | $12,248 | $11,839 |
| 18 | $19,735 | $18,906 | $18,124 | $17,387 | $16,691 | $16,034 | $15,413 | $14,826 | $14,270 | $13,744 | $13,246 | $12,774 | $12,326 |
| 19 | $20,979 | $20,050 | $19,178 | $18,357 | $17,585 | $16,858 | $16,172 | $15,526 | $14,916 | $14,340 | $13,796 | $13,282 | $12,795 |
| 20 | $22,239 | $21,206 | $20,237 | $19,328 | $18,476 | $17,675 | $16,922 | $16,215 | $15,549 | $14,922 | $14,331 | $13,773 | $13,247 |
| 21 | $23,518 | $22,371 | $21,301 | $20,299 | $19,363 | $18,485 | $17,663 | $16,892 | $16,168 | $15,489 | $14,850 | $14,249 | $13,683 |
| 22 | $24,813 | $23,548 | $22,370 | $21,271 | $20,246 | $19,289 | $18,395 | $17,558 | $16,775 | $16,041 | $15,354 | $14,708 | $14,102 |
| 23 | $26,126 | $24,736 | $23,444 | $22,243 | $21,127 | $20,087 | $19,117 | $18,213 | $17,369 | $16,580 | $15,843 | $15,152 | $14,506 |

## Inputs

| | 0.0% | 0.5% | 1.0% | 1.5% | 2.0% | 2.5% | 3.0% | 3.5% | 4.0% | 4.5% | 5.0% | 5.5% | 6.0% |
|---|---|---|---|---|---|---|---|---|---|---|---|---|---|
| R=real rate of return | 0.0% | | | | | | | | | | | | |
| T=tax rate | 10.0% | | | | | | | | | | | | |
| A=annual admin. fee | 1.0% | | | | | | | | | | | | |
| I=inflation | 4.0% | | | | | | | | | | | | |
| | 1.026 | 1.0305 | 1.035 | 1.0395 | 1.044 | 1.0485 | 1.053 | 1.0575 | 1.062 | 1.0665 | 1.071 | 1.0755 | 1.08 |
| E=expenses to start (ann) | $1,000 | $1,000 | $1,000 | $1,000 | $1,000 | $1,000 | $1,000 | $1,000 | $1,000 | $1,000 | $1,000 | $1,000 | $1,000 |

Figures assume that expenses are all taken out at end of each year.

| Rate of Return (Nominal): Life Expectancies | 4.0% | 4.5% | 5.0% | 5.5% | 6.0% | 6.5% | 7.0% | 7.5% | 8.0% | 8.5% | 9.0% | 9.5% | 10.0% |
|---|---|---|---|---|---|---|---|---|---|---|---|---|---|
| 24 | $27,458 | $25,934 | $24,523 | $23,216 | $22,003 | $20,877 | $19,831 | $18,857 | $17,951 | $17,106 | $16,318 | $15,582 | $14,894 |
| 25 | $28,807 | $27,144 | $25,608 | $24,189 | $22,877 | $21,662 | $20,536 | $19,491 | $18,521 | $17,619 | $16,779 | $15,997 | $15,269 |
| 26 | $30,175 | $28,364 | $26,698 | $25,163 | $23,747 | $22,440 | $21,232 | $20,114 | $19,079 | $18,119 | $17,227 | $16,399 | $15,629 |
| 27 | $31,561 | $29,596 | $27,793 | $26,137 | $24,614 | $23,212 | $21,920 | $20,727 | $19,625 | $18,606 | $17,662 | $16,788 | $15,976 |
| 28 | $32,966 | $30,839 | $28,894 | $27,112 | $25,478 | $23,978 | $22,599 | $21,330 | $20,160 | $19,081 | $18,085 | $17,163 | $16,310 |
| 29 | $34,391 | $32,094 | $29,999 | $28,087 | $26,338 | $24,737 | $23,269 | $21,922 | $20,684 | $19,545 | $18,495 | $17,527 | $16,632 |
| 30 | $35,835 | $33,360 | $31,111 | $29,062 | $27,195 | $25,490 | $23,932 | $22,505 | $21,197 | $19,997 | $18,894 | $17,878 | $16,942 |
| 31 | $37,298 | $34,638 | $32,227 | $30,038 | $28,049 | $26,237 | $24,586 | $23,078 | $21,700 | $20,438 | $19,280 | $18,218 | $17,240 |
| 32 | $38,782 | $35,928 | $33,349 | $31,015 | $28,899 | $26,978 | $25,232 | $23,642 | $22,192 | $20,867 | $19,656 | $18,546 | $17,528 |
| 33 | $40,286 | $37,230 | $34,476 | $31,992 | $29,746 | $27,713 | $25,870 | $24,196 | $22,674 | $21,287 | $20,021 | $18,864 | $17,805 |
| 34 | $41,810 | $38,543 | $35,609 | $32,969 | $30,590 | $28,442 | $26,500 | $24,742 | $23,146 | $21,695 | $20,375 | $19,171 | $18,071 |
| 35 | $43,355 | $39,869 | $36,747 | $33,947 | $31,431 | $29,166 | $27,123 | $25,278 | $23,608 | $22,094 | $20,719 | $19,468 | $18,328 |
| 36 | $44,922 | $41,207 | $37,891 | $34,925 | $32,268 | $29,883 | $27,738 | $25,805 | $24,060 | $22,483 | $21,053 | $19,755 | $18,575 |
| 37 | $46,509 | $42,557 | $39,040 | $35,904 | $33,102 | $30,594 | $28,345 | $26,324 | $24,504 | $22,862 | $21,377 | $20,033 | $18,813 |
| 38 | $48,119 | $43,920 | $40,195 | $36,883 | $33,933 | $31,300 | $28,945 | $26,834 | $24,938 | $23,231 | $21,692 | $20,301 | $19,042 |
| 39 | $49,750 | $45,295 | $41,355 | $37,863 | $34,761 | $32,000 | $29,537 | $27,335 | $25,363 | $23,592 | $21,998 | $20,561 | $19,263 |
| 40 | $51,403 | $46,683 | $42,521 | $38,843 | $35,586 | $32,694 | $30,122 | $27,828 | $25,779 | $23,943 | $22,295 | $20,812 | $19,475 |
| 41 | $53,079 | $48,084 | $43,693 | $39,824 | $36,407 | $33,383 | $30,700 | $28,314 | $26,186 | $24,286 | $22,583 | $21,055 | $19,680 |
| 42 | $54,778 | $49,498 | $44,870 | $40,805 | $37,226 | $34,066 | $31,270 | $28,791 | $26,586 | $24,620 | $22,863 | $21,290 | $19,877 |
| 43 | $56,500 | $50,924 | $46,053 | $41,787 | $38,041 | $34,744 | $31,834 | $29,260 | $26,976 | $24,946 | $23,135 | $21,517 | $20,067 |
| 44 | $58,246 | $52,364 | $47,242 | $42,769 | $38,853 | $35,416 | $32,391 | $29,721 | $27,359 | $25,264 | $23,399 | $21,737 | $20,249 |
| 45 | $60,015 | $53,817 | $48,436 | $43,751 | $39,662 | $36,082 | $32,941 | $30,175 | $27,734 | $25,574 | $23,656 | $21,949 | $20,425 |
| 46 | $61,809 | $55,284 | $49,636 | $44,734 | $40,468 | $36,744 | $33,484 | $30,621 | $28,101 | $25,876 | $23,905 | $22,154 | $20,595 |

# Chart Six

## Starting Portfolio Needed to Fund Various Annual Expenses Assuming 1% Trustee Fee and 10% Tax Rate (continued)

### Inputs

| | | | | | | | | | | | | | |
|---|---|---|---|---|---|---|---|---|---|---|---|---|---|
| R=real rate of return | 0.0% | 0.5% | 1.0% | 1.5% | 2.0% | 2.5% | 3.0% | 3.5% | 4.0% | 4.5% | 5.0% | 5.5% | 6.0% |
| T=tax rate | 10.0% | | | | | | | | | | | | |
| A=annual admin. fee | 1.0% | | | | | | | | | | | | |
| I=inflation | 4.0% | | | | | | | | | | | | |
| E=expenses to start (ann) | 1.026 | 1.0305 | 1.035 | 1.0395 | 1.044 | 1.0485 | 1.053 | 1.0575 | 1.062 | 1.0665 | 1.071 | 1.0755 | 1.08 |
| | $1,000 | $1,000 | $1,000 | $1,000 | $1,000 | $1,000 | $1,000 | $1,000 | $1,000 | $1,000 | $1,000 | $1,000 | $1,000 |

Figures assume that expenses are all taken out at end of each year.

### Rate of Return (Nominal):

| Life Expectancies | 4.0% | 4.5% | 5.0% | 5.5% | 6.0% | 6.5% | 7.0% | 7.5% | 8.0% | 8.5% | 9.0% | 9.5% | 10.0% |
|---|---|---|---|---|---|---|---|---|---|---|---|---|---|
| 47 | $63,627 | $56,764 | $50,842 | $45,718 | $41,271 | $37,400 | $34,020 | $31,060 | $28,461 | $26,170 | $24,147 | $22,353 | $20,758 |
| 48 | $65,470 | $58,258 | $52,054 | $46,702 | $42,070 | $38,050 | $34,550 | $31,492 | $28,813 | $26,458 | $24,381 | $22,545 | $20,915 |
| 49 | $67,338 | $59,765 | $53,272 | $47,686 | $42,867 | $38,695 | $35,073 | $31,916 | $29,157 | $26,738 | $24,609 | $22,730 | $21,066 |
| 50 | $69,232 | $61,286 | $54,495 | $48,671 | $43,661 | $39,335 | $35,589 | $32,334 | $29,495 | $27,011 | $24,831 | $22,910 | $21,212 |
| 51 | $71,151 | $62,822 | $55,725 | $49,657 | $44,451 | $39,970 | $36,100 | $32,744 | $29,826 | $27,278 | $25,046 | $23,083 | $21,352 |
| 52 | $73,096 | $64,371 | $56,960 | $50,643 | $45,239 | $40,600 | $36,604 | $33,148 | $30,149 | $27,538 | $25,254 | $23,251 | $21,487 |
| 53 | $75,068 | $65,935 | $58,201 | $51,629 | $46,023 | $41,225 | $37,101 | $33,545 | $30,467 | $27,791 | $25,457 | $23,414 | $21,617 |
| 54 | $77,067 | $67,513 | $59,449 | $52,616 | $46,805 | $41,844 | $37,593 | $33,936 | $30,777 | $28,038 | $25,654 | $23,571 | $21,743 |
| 55 | $79,094 | $69,106 | $60,702 | $53,603 | $47,583 | $42,459 | $38,079 | $34,320 | $31,081 | $28,279 | $25,845 | $23,722 | $21,863 |
| 56 | $81,148 | $70,714 | $61,961 | $54,591 | $48,359 | $43,068 | $38,558 | $34,697 | $31,379 | $28,514 | $26,031 | $23,869 | $21,980 |
| 57 | $83,230 | $72,336 | $63,227 | $55,579 | $49,131 | $43,673 | $39,032 | $35,069 | $31,670 | $28,743 | $26,211 | $24,011 | $22,091 |
| 58 | $85,340 | $73,973 | $64,499 | $56,568 | $49,901 | $44,272 | $39,500 | $35,434 | $31,956 | $28,967 | $26,386 | $24,148 | $22,199 |
| 59 | $87,479 | $75,626 | $65,776 | $57,557 | $50,668 | $44,867 | $39,962 | $35,793 | $32,236 | $29,185 | $26,556 | $24,281 | $22,303 |
| 60 | $89,647 | $77,293 | $67,060 | $58,547 | $51,431 | $45,457 | $40,418 | $36,147 | $32,509 | $29,397 | $26,721 | $24,409 | $22,403 |
| 61 | $91,845 | $78,976 | $68,350 | $59,537 | $52,192 | $46,043 | $40,869 | $36,494 | $32,778 | $29,604 | $26,881 | $24,533 | $22,499 |
| 62 | $94,073 | $80,675 | $69,647 | $60,528 | $52,950 | $46,623 | $41,314 | $36,836 | $33,040 | $29,806 | $27,037 | $24,653 | $22,592 |
| 63 | $96,332 | $82,389 | $70,949 | $61,519 | $53,705 | $47,199 | $41,753 | $37,172 | $33,297 | $30,003 | $27,188 | $24,770 | $22,681 |
| 64 | $98,621 | $84,119 | $72,258 | $62,510 | $54,457 | $47,770 | $42,187 | $37,502 | $33,549 | $30,195 | $27,335 | $24,882 | $22,767 |
| 65 | $100,941 | $85,865 | $73,574 | $63,502 | $55,206 | $48,336 | $42,616 | $37,827 | $33,796 | $30,383 | $27,477 | $24,990 | $22,849 |
| 66 | $103,293 | $87,627 | $74,895 | $64,495 | $55,953 | $48,898 | $43,040 | $38,147 | $34,037 | $30,566 | $27,616 | $25,095 | $22,929 |
| 67 | $105,677 | $89,405 | $76,223 | $65,488 | $56,696 | $49,456 | $43,458 | $38,461 | $34,274 | $30,744 | $27,750 | $25,197 | $23,006 |
| 68 | $108,094 | $91,199 | $77,558 | $66,481 | $57,437 | $50,008 | $43,871 | $38,771 | $34,505 | $30,917 | $27,881 | $25,295 | $23,080 |
| 69 | $110,543 | $93,011 | $78,899 | $67,475 | $58,175 | $50,557 | $44,279 | $39,075 | $34,732 | $31,087 | $28,007 | $25,390 | $23,151 |

## Inputs

| | |
|---|---|
| R=real rate of return | 0.0% |
| T=tax rate | 10.0% |
| A=annual admin. fee | 1.0% |
| I=inflation | 4.0% |

| | 6.0% | 5.5% | 5.0% | 4.5% | 4.0% | 3.5% | 3.0% | 2.5% | 2.0% | 1.5% | 1.0% | 0.5% |
|---|---|---|---|---|---|---|---|---|---|---|---|---|
| | 1.08 | 1.0755 | 1.071 | 1.0665 | 1.062 | 1.0575 | 1.053 | 1.0485 | 1.044 | 1.0395 | 1.035 | 1.0305 |
| E=expenses to start (ann) | $1,000 | $1,000 | $1,000 | $1,000 | $1,000 | $1,000 | $1,000 | $1,000 | $1,000 | $1,000 | $1,000 | $1,000 |

Figures assume that expenses are all taken out at end of each year.

## Rate of Return (Nominal):

| Life Expectancies | 10.0% | 9.5% | 9.0% | 8.5% | 8.0% | 7.5% | 7.0% | 6.5% | 6.0% | 5.5% | 5.0% | 4.5% | 4.0% |
|---|---|---|---|---|---|---|---|---|---|---|---|---|---|
| 70 | $23,219 | $25,481 | $28,130 | $31,252 | $34,954 | $39,374 | $44,682 | $51,101 | $58,910 | $68,470 | $80,246 | $94,838 | $113,026 |
| 71 | $23,285 | $25,570 | $28,250 | $31,413 | $35,172 | $39,668 | $45,080 | $51,640 | $59,642 | $69,465 | $81,600 | $96,683 | $115,543 |
| 72 | $23,349 | $25,656 | $28,366 | $31,570 | $35,385 | $39,957 | $45,474 | $52,175 | $60,371 | $70,460 | $82,960 | $98,545 | $118,095 |
| 73 | $23,410 | $25,739 | $28,479 | $31,723 | $35,594 | $40,241 | $45,862 | $52,706 | $61,098 | $71,456 | $84,327 | $100,424 | $120,681 |
| 74 | $23,469 | $25,819 | $28,588 | $31,873 | $35,798 | $40,521 | $46,245 | $53,233 | $61,821 | $72,452 | $85,701 | $102,320 | $123,302 |
| 75 | $23,525 | $25,897 | $28,694 | $32,019 | $35,998 | $40,796 | $46,624 | $53,755 | $62,542 | $73,449 | $87,081 | $104,234 | $125,959 |
| 76 | $23,580 | $25,972 | $28,797 | $32,161 | $36,194 | $41,067 | $46,998 | $54,273 | $63,261 | $74,447 | $88,468 | $106,165 | $128,653 |
| 77 | $23,633 | $26,044 | $28,897 | $32,299 | $36,386 | $41,333 | $47,368 | $54,786 | $63,976 | $75,444 | $89,861 | $108,114 | $131,383 |
| 78 | $23,683 | $26,114 | $28,995 | $32,434 | $36,573 | $41,594 | $47,732 | $55,296 | $64,689 | $76,443 | $91,262 | $110,081 | $134,150 |
| 79 | $23,732 | $26,182 | $29,089 | $32,566 | $36,757 | $41,851 | $48,093 | $55,801 | $65,399 | $77,441 | $92,669 | $112,066 | $136,955 |
| 80 | $23,779 | $26,248 | $29,181 | $32,694 | $36,938 | $42,105 | $48,449 | $56,303 | $66,106 | $78,441 | $94,082 | $114,070 | $139,799 |
| 81 | $23,824 | $26,311 | $29,270 | $32,820 | $37,114 | $42,353 | $48,800 | $56,800 | $66,811 | $79,440 | $95,503 | $116,092 | $142,681 |
| 82 | $23,868 | $26,372 | $29,356 | $32,942 | $37,287 | $42,598 | $49,147 | $57,293 | $67,513 | $80,441 | $96,931 | $118,132 | $145,603 |
| 83 | $23,910 | $26,432 | $29,440 | $33,061 | $37,456 | $42,839 | $49,490 | $57,783 | $68,212 | $81,441 | $98,365 | $120,192 | $148,564 |
| 84 | $23,950 | $26,489 | $29,522 | $33,177 | $37,622 | $43,076 | $49,829 | $58,268 | $68,908 | $82,443 | $99,807 | $122,270 | $151,566 |
| 85 | $23,989 | $26,545 | $29,601 | $33,290 | $37,784 | $43,308 | $50,164 | $58,749 | $69,602 | $83,444 | $101,255 | $124,368 | $154,609 |
| 86 | $24,026 | $26,598 | $29,678 | $33,401 | $37,943 | $43,537 | $50,494 | $59,227 | $70,293 | $84,446 | $102,710 | $126,485 | $157,693 |
| 87 | $24,062 | $26,650 | $29,753 | $33,509 | $38,098 | $43,762 | $50,820 | $59,700 | $70,982 | $85,449 | $104,173 | $128,621 | $160,819 |
| 88 | $24,097 | $26,700 | $29,825 | $33,614 | $38,251 | $43,984 | $51,142 | $60,170 | $71,668 | $86,452 | $105,642 | $130,777 | $163,989 |
| 89 | $24,131 | $26,749 | $29,896 | $33,716 | $38,400 | $44,202 | $51,461 | $60,636 | $72,351 | $87,456 | $107,119 | $132,953 | $167,201 |
| 90 | $24,163 | $26,795 | $29,964 | $33,816 | $38,546 | $44,416 | $51,775 | $61,098 | $73,032 | $88,460 | $108,602 | $135,149 | $170,457 |

# CHART SEVEN

## STARTING PORTFOLIO NEEDED TO FUND VARIOUS ANNUAL EXPENSES ASSUMING 1% TRUSTEE FEE AND 20% TAX RATE

**Inputs**

| | |
|---|---|
| R=real rate of return | 0.0% |
| T=tax rate | 20.0% |
| A=annual admin. fee | 1.0% |
| I=inflation | 4.0% |

| | 0.0% | 0.5% | 1.0% | 1.5% | 2.0% | 2.5% | 3.0% | 3.5% | 4.0% | 4.5% | 5.0% | 5.5% | 6.0% |
|---|---|---|---|---|---|---|---|---|---|---|---|---|---|
| | 1.022 | 1.026 | 1.03 | 1.034 | 1.038 | 1.042 | 1.046 | 1.05 | 1.054 | 1.058 | 1.062 | 1.066 | 1.07 |
| E=expenses to start (ann) | $1,000 | $1,000 | $1,000 | $1,000 | $1,000 | $1,000 | $1,000 | $1,000 | $1,000 | $1,000 | $1,000 | $1,000 | $1,000 |

Figures assume that expenses are all taken out at end of each year.

**Rate of Return (Nominal):**

| Life Expectancies | 4.0% | 4.5% | 5.0% | 5.5% | 6.0% | 6.5% | 7.0% | 7.5% | 8.0% | 8.5% | 9.0% | 9.5% | 10.0% |
|---|---|---|---|---|---|---|---|---|---|---|---|---|---|
| 1 | $978 | $975 | $971 | $967 | $963 | $960 | $956 | $952 | $949 | $945 | $942 | $938 | $935 |
| 2 | $1,974 | $1,963 | $1,951 | $1,940 | $1,929 | $1,918 | $1,907 | $1,896 | $1,885 | $1,874 | $1,864 | $1,853 | $1,843 |
| 3 | $2,987 | $2,964 | $2,941 | $2,918 | $2,896 | $2,874 | $2,852 | $2,830 | $2,809 | $2,788 | $2,767 | $2,746 | $2,726 |
| 4 | $4,019 | $3,979 | $3,940 | $3,902 | $3,865 | $3,828 | $3,791 | $3,755 | $3,720 | $3,685 | $3,651 | $3,617 | $3,584 |
| 5 | $5,068 | $5,008 | $4,950 | $4,892 | $4,836 | $4,780 | $4,726 | $4,672 | $4,619 | $4,568 | $4,517 | $4,467 | $4,418 |
| 6 | $6,135 | $6,051 | $5,968 | $5,888 | $5,808 | $5,731 | $5,655 | $5,580 | $5,507 | $5,435 | $5,365 | $5,296 | $5,229 |
| 7 | $7,222 | $7,108 | $6,997 | $6,889 | $6,783 | $6,679 | $6,578 | $6,479 | $6,383 | $6,288 | $6,196 | $6,105 | $6,017 |
| 8 | $8,328 | $8,180 | $8,036 | $7,896 | $7,759 | $7,626 | $7,496 | $7,370 | $7,246 | $7,126 | $7,009 | $6,894 | $6,783 |
| 9 | $9,453 | $9,266 | $9,085 | $8,909 | $8,738 | $8,571 | $8,409 | $8,252 | $8,099 | $7,950 | $7,805 | $7,664 | $7,527 |
| 10 | $10,598 | $10,367 | $10,144 | $9,928 | $9,718 | $9,514 | $9,317 | $9,126 | $8,940 | $8,760 | $8,585 | $8,415 | $8,251 |
| 11 | $11,763 | $11,483 | $11,213 | $10,952 | $10,700 | $10,456 | $10,220 | $9,991 | $9,770 | $9,556 | $9,349 | $9,148 | $8,954 |
| 12 | $12,949 | $12,615 | $12,293 | $11,983 | $11,684 | $11,396 | $11,117 | $10,849 | $10,589 | $10,339 | $10,097 | $9,863 | $9,637 |
| 13 | $14,155 | $13,762 | $13,383 | $13,020 | $12,670 | $12,333 | $12,009 | $11,698 | $11,397 | $11,108 | $10,829 | $10,561 | $10,302 |
| 14 | $15,383 | $14,924 | $14,484 | $14,062 | $13,658 | $13,269 | $12,897 | $12,539 | $12,195 | $11,864 | $11,547 | $11,241 | $10,948 |
| 15 | $16,632 | $16,102 | $15,596 | $15,111 | $14,647 | $14,204 | $13,779 | $13,372 | $12,981 | $12,608 | $12,249 | $11,905 | $11,575 |
| 16 | $17,904 | $17,297 | $16,718 | $16,166 | $15,639 | $15,136 | $14,656 | $14,197 | $13,758 | $13,338 | $12,937 | $12,553 | $12,185 |
| 17 | $19,198 | $18,507 | $17,851 | $17,227 | $16,633 | $16,067 | $15,528 | $15,014 | $14,524 | $14,057 | $13,611 | $13,185 | $12,778 |
| 18 | $20,514 | $19,735 | $18,995 | $18,294 | $17,628 | $16,996 | $16,395 | $15,823 | $15,280 | $14,763 | $14,270 | $13,801 | $13,354 |
| 19 | $21,854 | $20,979 | $20,151 | $19,367 | $18,625 | $17,923 | $17,256 | $16,625 | $16,026 | $15,457 | $14,916 | $14,403 | $13,915 |
| 20 | $23,217 | $22,239 | $21,317 | $20,447 | $19,625 | $18,848 | $18,114 | $17,419 | $16,761 | $16,139 | $15,549 | $14,990 | $14,459 |
| 21 | $24,605 | $23,518 | $22,495 | $21,532 | $20,626 | $19,771 | $18,966 | $18,205 | $17,488 | $16,809 | $16,168 | $15,562 | $14,988 |
| 22 | $26,016 | $24,813 | $23,684 | $22,625 | $21,629 | $20,693 | $19,813 | $18,984 | $18,204 | $17,469 | $16,775 | $16,121 | $15,503 |
| 23 | $27,453 | $26,126 | $24,885 | $23,723 | $22,634 | $21,613 | $20,655 | $19,756 | $18,911 | $18,117 | $17,369 | $16,665 | $16,003 |

## Inputs

| | |
|---|---|
| R=real rate of return | 0.0% |
| T=tax rate | 20.0% |
| A=annual admin. fee | 1.0% |
| I=inflation | 4.0% |

| G=1+(R+I)*(1-T)-A | 0.0% 1.022 | 0.5% 1.026 | 1.0% 1.03 | 1.5% 1.034 | 2.0% 1.038 | 2.5% 1.042 | 3.0% 1.046 | 3.5% 1.05 | 4.0% 1.054 | 4.5% 1.058 | 5.0% 1.062 | 5.5% 1.066 | 6.0% 1.07 |
|---|---|---|---|---|---|---|---|---|---|---|---|---|---|
| E=expenses to start (ann) | $1,000 | $1,000 | $1,000 | $1,000 | $1,000 | $1,000 | $1,000 | $1,000 | $1,000 | $1,000 | $1,000 | $1,000 | $1,000 |

Figures assume that expenses are all taken out at end of each year.

## Rate of Return (Nominal):

| Life Expectancies | 4.0% | 4.5% | 5.0% | 5.5% | 6.0% | 6.5% | 7.0% | 7.5% | 8.0% | 8.5% | 9.0% | 9.5% | 10.0% |
|---|---|---|---|---|---|---|---|---|---|---|---|---|---|
| 24 | $28,915 | $27,458 | $26,098 | $24,828 | $23,641 | $22,531 | $21,493 | $20,520 | $19,609 | $18,754 | $17,951 | $17,197 | $16,488 |
| 25 | $30,403 | $28,807 | $27,322 | $25,939 | $24,650 | $23,448 | $22,326 | $21,277 | $20,297 | $19,380 | $18,521 | $17,716 | $16,961 |
| 26 | $31,917 | $30,175 | $28,558 | $27,057 | $25,661 | $24,362 | $23,153 | $22,027 | $20,976 | $19,995 | $19,079 | $18,222 | $17,420 |
| 27 | $33,457 | $31,561 | $29,806 | $28,181 | $26,674 | $25,275 | $23,977 | $22,769 | $21,646 | $20,600 | $19,625 | $18,715 | $17,866 |
| 28 | $35,025 | $32,966 | $31,066 | $29,311 | $27,688 | $26,187 | $24,795 | $23,505 | $22,307 | $21,195 | $20,160 | $19,197 | $18,300 |
| 29 | $36,621 | $34,391 | $32,339 | $30,448 | $28,705 | $27,096 | $25,609 | $24,234 | $22,960 | $21,779 | $20,684 | $19,667 | $18,721 |
| 30 | $38,244 | $35,835 | $33,624 | $31,592 | $29,724 | $28,004 | $26,418 | $24,955 | $23,604 | $22,354 | $21,197 | $20,125 | $19,131 |
| 31 | $39,896 | $37,298 | $34,921 | $32,743 | $30,745 | $28,910 | $27,223 | $25,670 | $24,239 | $22,919 | $21,700 | $20,573 | $19,529 |
| 32 | $41,577 | $38,782 | $36,231 | $33,900 | $31,767 | $29,814 | $28,022 | $26,378 | $24,866 | $23,474 | $22,192 | $21,009 | $19,916 |
| 33 | $43,288 | $40,286 | $37,554 | $35,064 | $32,792 | $30,716 | $28,818 | $27,079 | $25,484 | $24,020 | $22,674 | $21,435 | $20,292 |
| 34 | $45,029 | $41,810 | $38,889 | $36,234 | $33,818 | $31,617 | $29,608 | $27,773 | $26,094 | $24,557 | $23,146 | $21,850 | $20,658 |
| 35 | $46,800 | $43,355 | $40,237 | $37,412 | $34,847 | $32,516 | $30,395 | $28,461 | $26,697 | $25,084 | $23,608 | $22,255 | $21,013 |
| 36 | $48,603 | $44,922 | $41,599 | $38,596 | $35,877 | $33,413 | $31,176 | $29,143 | $27,291 | $25,602 | $24,060 | $22,650 | $21,359 |
| 37 | $50,438 | $46,509 | $42,974 | $39,787 | $36,910 | $34,309 | $31,954 | $29,817 | $27,877 | $26,112 | $24,504 | $23,036 | $21,694 |
| 38 | $52,304 | $48,119 | $44,362 | $40,985 | $37,944 | $35,203 | $32,726 | $30,486 | $28,456 | $26,613 | $24,938 | $23,412 | $22,021 |
| 39 | $54,204 | $49,750 | $45,763 | $42,190 | $38,981 | $36,095 | $33,495 | $31,148 | $29,026 | $27,105 | $25,363 | $23,779 | $22,338 |
| 40 | $56,137 | $51,403 | $47,179 | $43,402 | $40,019 | $36,985 | $34,258 | $31,804 | $29,590 | $27,589 | $25,779 | $24,137 | $22,646 |
| 41 | $58,104 | $53,079 | $48,607 | $44,621 | $41,060 | $37,874 | $35,018 | $32,453 | $30,145 | $28,065 | $26,186 | $24,487 | $22,946 |
| 42 | $60,106 | $54,778 | $50,050 | $45,847 | $42,102 | $38,761 | $35,773 | $33,096 | $30,694 | $28,533 | $26,586 | $24,828 | $23,237 |
| 43 | $62,143 | $56,500 | $51,507 | $47,080 | $43,147 | $39,646 | $36,524 | $33,734 | $31,235 | $28,993 | $26,976 | $25,160 | $23,520 |
| 44 | $64,216 | $58,246 | $52,978 | $48,320 | $44,194 | $40,530 | $37,270 | $34,365 | $31,769 | $29,444 | $27,359 | $25,484 | $23,795 |
| 45 | $66,326 | $60,015 | $54,463 | $49,568 | $45,242 | $41,412 | $38,013 | $34,990 | $32,295 | $29,889 | $27,734 | $25,801 | $24,063 |
| 46 | $68,472 | $61,809 | $55,963 | $50,822 | $46,293 | $42,292 | $38,751 | $35,609 | $32,815 | $30,325 | $28,101 | $26,110 | $24,323 |
| 47 | $70,657 | $63,627 | $57,477 | $52,084 | $47,345 | $43,170 | $39,484 | $36,222 | $33,328 | $30,755 | $28,461 | $26,411 | $24,575 |

APPENDIX ONE

## STARTING PORTFOLIO NEEDED TO FUND VARIOUS ANNUAL EXPENSES
### ASSUMING 1% TRUSTEE FEE AND 20% TAX RATE (CONTINUED)

**Inputs**

| | | | | | | | | | | | | | |
|---|---|---|---|---|---|---|---|---|---|---|---|---|---|
| R=real rate of return | 0.0% | 0.5% | 1.0% | 1.5% | 2.0% | 2.5% | 3.0% | 3.5% | 4.0% | 4.5% | 5.0% | 5.5% | 6.0% |
| T=tax rate | 20.0% | | | | | | | | | | | | |
| A=annual admin. fee | 1.0% | | | | | | | | | | | | |
| I=inflation | 4.0% | | | | | | | | | | | | |
| | 1.022 | 1.026 | 1.03 | 1.034 | 1.038 | 1.042 | 1.046 | 1.05 | 1.054 | 1.058 | 1.062 | 1.066 | 1.07 |
| E=expenses to start (ann) | $1,000 | $1,000 | $1,000 | $1,000 | $1,000 | $1,000 | $1,000 | $1,000 | $1,000 | $1,000 | $1,000 | $1,000 | $1,000 |

Figures assume that expenses are all taken out at end of each year.

**Rate of Return (Nominal):**

| Life Expectancies | 4.0% | 4.5% | 5.0% | 5.5% | 6.0% | 6.5% | 7.0% | 7.5% | 8.0% | 8.5% | 9.0% | 9.5% | 10.0% |
|---|---|---|---|---|---|---|---|---|---|---|---|---|---|
| 48 | $72,880 | $65,470 | $59,006 | $53,354 | $48,400 | $44,047 | $40,214 | $36,830 | $33,834 | $31,177 | $28,813 | $26,705 | $24,821 |
| 49 | $75,142 | $67,338 | $60,550 | $54,631 | $49,456 | $44,922 | $40,939 | $37,431 | $34,334 | $31,591 | $29,157 | $26,992 | $25,059 |
| 50 | $77,444 | $69,232 | $62,108 | $55,915 | $50,515 | $45,796 | $41,660 | $38,027 | $34,826 | $31,999 | $29,495 | $27,271 | $25,291 |
| 51 | $79,786 | $71,151 | $63,682 | $57,206 | $51,576 | $46,668 | $42,378 | $38,617 | $35,312 | $32,400 | $29,826 | $27,544 | $25,517 |
| 52 | $82,170 | $73,096 | $65,271 | $58,505 | $52,639 | $47,538 | $43,090 | $39,202 | $35,792 | $32,794 | $30,149 | $27,811 | $25,736 |
| 53 | $84,596 | $75,068 | $66,876 | $59,812 | $53,703 | $48,406 | $43,799 | $39,781 | $36,266 | $33,181 | $30,467 | $28,070 | $25,949 |
| 54 | $87,064 | $77,067 | $68,496 | $61,126 | $54,770 | $49,273 | $44,504 | $40,354 | $36,733 | $33,562 | $30,777 | $28,324 | $26,156 |
| 55 | $89,576 | $79,094 | $70,132 | $62,448 | $55,839 | $50,138 | $45,205 | $40,922 | $37,193 | $33,936 | $31,081 | $28,571 | $26,357 |
| 56 | $92,132 | $81,148 | $71,784 | $63,777 | $56,910 | $51,002 | $45,902 | $41,485 | $37,648 | $34,304 | $31,379 | $28,812 | $26,553 |
| 57 | $94,733 | $83,230 | $73,452 | $65,115 | $57,983 | $51,863 | $46,594 | $42,042 | $38,097 | $34,665 | $31,670 | $29,048 | $26,743 |
| 58 | $97,380 | $85,340 | $75,136 | $66,460 | $59,058 | $52,724 | $47,283 | $42,594 | $38,540 | $35,021 | $31,956 | $29,277 | $26,928 |
| 59 | $100,074 | $87,479 | $76,836 | $67,812 | $60,136 | $53,582 | $47,968 | $43,141 | $38,976 | $35,370 | $32,236 | $29,501 | $27,107 |
| 60 | $102,815 | $89,647 | $78,553 | $69,173 | $61,215 | $54,439 | $48,649 | $43,683 | $39,408 | $35,713 | $32,509 | $29,720 | $27,282 |
| 61 | $105,604 | $91,845 | $80,286 | $70,541 | $62,296 | $55,294 | $49,326 | $44,219 | $39,833 | $36,051 | $32,778 | $29,933 | $27,452 |
| 62 | $108,443 | $94,073 | $82,037 | $71,918 | $63,380 | $56,148 | $49,999 | $44,750 | $40,253 | $36,383 | $33,040 | $30,141 | $27,617 |
| 63 | $111,331 | $96,332 | $83,804 | $73,302 | $64,465 | $57,000 | $50,668 | $45,276 | $40,667 | $36,709 | $33,297 | $30,344 | $27,777 |
| 64 | $114,270 | $98,621 | $85,589 | $74,695 | $65,553 | $57,850 | $51,333 | $45,798 | $41,075 | $37,030 | $33,549 | $30,542 | $27,933 |
| 65 | $117,261 | $100,941 | $87,390 | $76,095 | $66,642 | $58,699 | $51,995 | $46,314 | $41,478 | $37,345 | $33,796 | $30,735 | $28,084 |
| 66 | $120,305 | $103,293 | $89,210 | $77,504 | $67,734 | $59,546 | $52,653 | $46,825 | $41,876 | $37,655 | $34,037 | $30,924 | $28,231 |
| 67 | $123,402 | $105,677 | $91,047 | $78,921 | $68,828 | $60,391 | $53,307 | $47,332 | $42,269 | $37,959 | $34,274 | $31,107 | $28,374 |
| 68 | $126,554 | $108,094 | $92,902 | $80,346 | $69,924 | $61,235 | $53,957 | $47,833 | $42,656 | $38,259 | $34,505 | $31,287 | $28,513 |
| 69 | $129,762 | $110,543 | $94,774 | $81,779 | $71,022 | $62,077 | $54,603 | $48,330 | $43,038 | $38,553 | $34,732 | $31,462 | $28,648 |

## Inputs

| | | | | | | | | | | | | | |
|---|---|---|---|---|---|---|---|---|---|---|---|---|---|
| R=real rate of return | 0.0% | | | | | | | | | | | | |
| T=tax rate | 20.0% | | | | | | | | | | | | |
| A=annual admin. fee | 1.0% | | | | | | | | | | | | |
| I=inflation | 4.0% | | | | | | | | | | | | |
| | **0.0%** | **0.5%** | **1.0%** | **1.5%** | **2.0%** | **2.5%** | **3.0%** | **3.5%** | **4.0%** | **4.5%** | **5.0%** | **5.5%** | **6.0%** |
| E=expenses to start (ann) | 1.022 | 1.026 | 1.03 | 1.034 | 1.038 | 1.042 | 1.046 | 1.05 | 1.054 | 1.058 | 1.062 | 1.066 | 1.07 |
| | $1,000 | $1,000 | $1,000 | $1,000 | $1,000 | $1,000 | $1,000 | $1,000 | $1,000 | $1,000 | $1,000 | $1,000 | $1,000 |

Figures assume that expenses are all taken out at end of each year.

## Rate of Return (Nominal):

| Life Expectancies | 4.0% | 4.5% | 5.0% | 5.5% | 6.0% | 6.5% | 7.0% | 7.5% | 8.0% | 8.5% | 9.0% | 9.5% | 10.0% |
|---|---|---|---|---|---|---|---|---|---|---|---|---|---|
| 70 | $133,026 | $113,026 | $96,665 | $83,221 | $72,122 | $62,917 | $55,246 | $48,822 | $43,415 | $38,842 | $34,954 | $31,633 | $28,780 |
| 71 | $136,347 | $115,543 | $98,575 | $84,671 | $73,225 | $63,756 | $55,885 | $49,309 | $43,787 | $39,127 | $35,172 | $31,799 | $28,907 |
| 72 | $139,727 | $118,095 | $100,503 | $86,129 | $74,329 | $64,594 | $56,521 | $49,792 | $44,155 | $39,406 | $35,385 | $31,962 | $29,032 |
| 73 | $143,166 | $120,681 | $102,449 | $87,596 | $75,436 | $65,429 | $57,153 | $50,270 | $44,517 | $39,681 | $35,594 | $32,120 | $29,152 |
| 74 | $146,666 | $123,302 | $104,415 | $89,072 | $76,545 | $66,264 | $57,781 | $50,744 | $44,874 | $39,951 | $35,798 | $32,275 | $29,269 |
| 75 | $150,228 | $125,959 | $106,399 | $90,556 | $77,656 | $67,096 | $58,405 | $51,213 | $45,227 | $40,216 | $35,998 | $32,426 | $29,383 |
| 76 | $153,852 | $128,653 | $108,403 | $92,048 | $78,769 | $67,927 | $59,026 | $51,678 | $45,575 | $40,477 | $36,194 | $32,573 | $29,494 |
| 77 | $157,541 | $131,383 | $110,427 | $93,550 | $79,884 | $68,756 | $59,644 | $52,138 | $45,918 | $40,734 | $36,386 | $32,717 | $29,602 |
| 78 | $161,294 | $134,150 | $112,470 | $95,060 | $81,001 | $69,584 | $60,258 | $52,594 | $46,257 | $40,986 | $36,573 | $32,857 | $29,706 |
| 79 | $165,113 | $136,955 | $114,532 | $96,578 | $82,120 | $70,410 | $60,868 | $53,045 | $46,592 | $41,234 | $36,757 | $32,993 | $29,808 |
| 80 | $169,000 | $139,799 | $116,615 | $98,106 | $83,242 | $71,235 | $61,475 | $53,492 | $46,922 | $41,478 | $36,938 | $33,127 | $29,907 |
| 81 | $172,955 | $142,681 | $118,718 | $99,642 | $84,366 | $72,058 | $62,078 | $53,935 | $47,247 | $41,717 | $37,114 | $33,257 | $30,003 |
| 82 | $176,979 | $145,603 | $120,842 | $101,187 | $85,492 | $72,879 | $62,678 | $54,374 | $47,568 | $41,952 | $37,287 | $33,384 | $30,096 |
| 83 | $181,075 | $148,564 | $122,986 | $102,742 | $86,620 | $73,699 | $63,275 | $54,809 | $47,885 | $42,184 | $37,456 | $33,508 | $30,187 |
| 84 | $185,242 | $151,566 | $125,151 | $104,305 | $87,750 | $74,517 | $63,868 | $55,239 | $48,198 | $42,411 | $37,622 | $33,628 | $30,275 |
| 85 | $189,483 | $154,609 | $127,337 | $105,877 | $88,883 | $75,334 | $64,458 | $55,665 | $48,506 | $42,635 | $37,784 | $33,746 | $30,361 |
| 86 | $193,799 | $157,693 | $129,544 | $107,459 | $90,017 | $76,149 | $65,044 | $56,088 | $48,811 | $42,855 | $37,943 | $33,861 | $30,444 |
| 87 | $198,191 | $160,819 | $131,773 | $109,050 | $91,154 | $76,962 | $65,627 | $56,506 | $49,111 | $43,071 | $38,098 | $33,974 | $30,525 |
| 88 | $202,660 | $163,989 | $134,023 | $110,650 | $92,293 | $77,774 | $66,206 | $56,920 | $49,408 | $43,283 | $38,251 | $34,083 | $30,604 |
| 89 | $207,208 | $167,201 | $136,295 | $112,259 | $93,434 | $78,585 | $66,783 | $57,330 | $49,700 | $43,492 | $38,400 | $34,190 | $30,681 |
| 90 | $211,836 | $170,457 | $138,589 | $113,877 | $94,578 | $79,394 | $67,356 | $57,737 | $49,989 | $43,697 | $38,546 | $34,294 | $30,755 |

# Chart Eight

## Starting Portfolio Needed to Fund Various Annual Expenses
### Assuming 1% Trustee Fee and 30% Tax Rate

**Inputs**

| | |
|---|---|
| R=real rate of return | 0.0% |
| T=tax rate | 30.0% |
| A=annual admin. fee | 1.0% |
| I=inflation | 4.0% |

| | 0.0% | 0.5% | 1.0% | 1.5% | 2.0% | 2.5% | 3.0% | 3.5% | 4.0% | 4.5% | 5.0% | 5.5% | 6.0% |
|---|---|---|---|---|---|---|---|---|---|---|---|---|---|
| E=expenses to start (ann) | 1.018 | 1.0215 | 1.025 | 1.0285 | 1.032 | 1.0355 | 1.039 | 1.0425 | 1.046 | 1.0495 | 1.053 | 1.0565 | 1.06 |
| | $1,000 | $1,000 | $1,000 | $1,000 | $1,000 | $1,000 | $1,000 | $1,000 | $1,000 | $1,000 | $1,000 | $1,000 | $1,000 |

Figures assume that expenses are all taken out at end of each year.

**Rate of Return (Nominal):**

| Life Expectancies | 4.0% | 4.5% | 5.0% | 5.5% | 6.0% | 6.5% | 7.0% | 7.5% | 8.0% | 8.5% | 9.0% | 9.5% | 10.0% |
|---|---|---|---|---|---|---|---|---|---|---|---|---|---|
| 1 | $982 | $979 | $976 | $972 | $969 | $966 | $962 | $959 | $956 | $953 | $950 | $947 | $943 |
| 2 | $1,986 | $1,976 | $1,965 | $1,955 | $1,945 | $1,936 | $1,926 | $1,916 | $1,907 | $1,897 | $1,888 | $1,878 | $1,869 |
| 3 | $3,011 | $2,990 | $2,970 | $2,950 | $2,930 | $2,910 | $2,890 | $2,871 | $2,852 | $2,833 | $2,814 | $2,795 | $2,777 |
| 4 | $4,058 | $4,023 | $3,989 | $3,955 | $3,921 | $3,888 | $3,855 | $3,823 | $3,791 | $3,760 | $3,729 | $3,698 | $3,668 |
| 5 | $5,129 | $5,075 | $5,023 | $4,971 | $4,921 | $4,871 | $4,822 | $4,773 | $4,726 | $4,679 | $4,633 | $4,587 | $4,542 |
| 6 | $6,222 | $6,146 | $6,072 | $5,999 | $5,928 | $5,858 | $5,789 | $5,721 | $5,655 | $5,589 | $5,525 | $5,462 | $5,400 |
| 7 | $7,338 | $7,236 | $7,137 | $7,039 | $6,943 | $6,849 | $6,757 | $6,667 | $6,578 | $6,491 | $6,406 | $6,323 | $6,242 |
| 8 | $8,479 | $8,346 | $8,217 | $8,090 | $7,966 | $7,844 | $7,726 | $7,610 | $7,496 | $7,386 | $7,277 | $7,171 | $7,067 |
| 9 | $9,645 | $9,477 | $9,312 | $9,152 | $8,996 | $8,844 | $8,696 | $8,551 | $8,409 | $8,271 | $8,137 | $8,005 | $7,877 |
| 10 | $10,836 | $10,627 | $10,424 | $10,227 | $10,035 | $9,848 | $9,666 | $9,489 | $9,317 | $9,149 | $8,986 | $8,827 | $8,672 |
| 11 | $12,052 | $11,799 | $11,552 | $11,314 | $11,082 | $10,857 | $10,638 | $10,426 | $10,220 | $10,019 | $9,825 | $9,636 | $9,452 |
| 12 | $13,295 | $12,991 | $12,697 | $12,412 | $12,137 | $11,870 | $11,611 | $11,360 | $11,117 | $10,882 | $10,653 | $10,432 | $10,217 |
| 13 | $14,565 | $14,205 | $13,859 | $13,524 | $13,200 | $12,887 | $12,585 | $12,292 | $12,009 | $11,736 | $11,471 | $11,215 | $10,967 |
| 14 | $15,862 | $15,442 | $15,037 | $14,647 | $14,271 | $13,909 | $13,559 | $13,222 | $12,897 | $12,583 | $12,279 | $11,987 | $11,704 |
| 15 | $17,187 | $16,700 | $16,233 | $15,783 | $15,351 | $14,935 | $14,535 | $14,149 | $13,779 | $13,421 | $13,077 | $12,746 | $12,426 |
| 16 | $18,540 | $17,982 | $17,446 | $16,932 | $16,439 | $15,965 | $15,511 | $15,075 | $14,656 | $14,253 | $13,866 | $13,493 | $13,135 |
| 17 | $19,923 | $19,286 | $18,677 | $18,093 | $17,535 | $17,001 | $16,488 | $15,998 | $15,528 | $15,077 | $14,644 | $14,229 | $13,831 |
| 18 | $21,336 | $20,614 | $19,926 | $19,268 | $18,640 | $18,040 | $17,467 | $16,919 | $16,395 | $15,893 | $15,413 | $14,954 | $14,513 |
| 19 | $22,780 | $21,967 | $21,193 | $20,456 | $19,754 | $19,084 | $18,446 | $17,837 | $17,256 | $16,702 | $16,172 | $15,666 | $15,183 |
| 20 | $24,254 | $23,344 | $22,479 | $21,657 | $20,876 | $20,133 | $19,426 | $18,754 | $18,114 | $17,504 | $16,922 | $16,368 | $15,840 |
| 21 | $25,761 | $24,745 | $23,783 | $22,871 | $22,006 | $21,186 | $20,407 | $19,668 | $18,966 | $18,298 | $17,663 | $17,059 | $16,484 |
| 22 | $27,300 | $26,172 | $25,107 | $24,099 | $23,146 | $22,244 | $21,390 | $20,580 | $19,813 | $19,085 | $18,395 | $17,739 | $17,117 |
| 23 | $28,872 | $27,625 | $26,450 | $25,341 | $24,294 | $23,306 | $22,373 | $21,490 | $20,655 | $19,865 | $19,117 | $18,409 | $17,737 |

**Inputs**

| | | | | | | | | | | | | | |
|---|---|---|---|---|---|---|---|---|---|---|---|---|---|
| R=real rate of return | 0.0% | 0.5% | 1.0% | 1.5% | 2.0% | 2.5% | 3.0% | 3.5% | 4.0% | 4.5% | 5.0% | 5.5% | 6.0% |
| T=tax rate | 30.0% | | | | | | | | | | | | |
| A=annual admin. fee | 1.0% | | | | | | | | | | | | |
| I=inflation | 4.0% | | | | | | | | | | | | |
| | 1.018 | 1.0215 | 1.025 | 1.0285 | 1.032 | 1.0355 | 1.039 | 1.0425 | 1.046 | 1.0495 | 1.053 | 1.0565 | 1.06 |
| E=expenses to start (ann) | $1,000 | $1,000 | $1,000 | $1,000 | $1,000 | $1,000 | $1,000 | $1,000 | $1,000 | $1,000 | $1,000 | $1,000 | $1,000 |

Figures assume that expenses are all taken out at end of each year.

| Rate of Return (Nominal): | 4.0% | 4.5% | 5.0% | 5.5% | 6.0% | 6.5% | 7.0% | 7.5% | 8.0% | 8.5% | 9.0% | 9.5% | 10.0% |
|---|---|---|---|---|---|---|---|---|---|---|---|---|---|
| **Life Expectancies** | | | | | | | | | | | | | |
| 24 | $30,478 | $29,105 | $27,813 | $26,597 | $25,452 | $24,373 | $23,357 | $22,398 | $21,493 | $20,638 | $19,831 | $19,068 | $18,346 |
| 25 | $32,119 | $30,611 | $29,195 | $27,866 | $26,618 | $25,445 | $24,342 | $23,303 | $22,326 | $21,404 | $20,536 | $19,717 | $18,943 |
| 26 | $33,796 | $32,144 | $30,598 | $29,150 | $27,793 | $26,521 | $25,327 | $24,207 | $23,153 | $22,163 | $21,232 | $20,355 | $19,529 |
| 27 | $35,509 | $33,705 | $32,021 | $30,448 | $28,978 | $27,602 | $26,314 | $25,108 | $23,977 | $22,916 | $21,920 | $20,984 | $20,104 |
| 28 | $37,258 | $35,294 | $33,466 | $31,761 | $30,172 | $28,688 | $27,302 | $26,007 | $24,795 | $23,661 | $22,599 | $21,603 | $20,668 |
| 29 | $39,046 | $36,913 | $34,931 | $33,089 | $31,374 | $29,778 | $28,291 | $26,904 | $25,609 | $24,400 | $23,269 | $22,212 | $21,222 |
| 30 | $40,872 | $38,560 | $36,418 | $34,431 | $32,587 | $30,873 | $29,281 | $27,798 | $26,418 | $25,132 | $23,932 | $22,811 | $21,765 |
| 31 | $42,738 | $40,237 | $37,926 | $35,788 | $33,808 | $31,973 | $30,271 | $28,691 | $27,223 | $25,857 | $24,586 | $23,402 | $22,297 |
| 32 | $44,643 | $41,945 | $39,457 | $37,161 | $35,039 | $33,078 | $31,263 | $29,581 | $28,022 | $26,576 | $25,232 | $23,983 | $22,820 |
| 33 | $46,591 | $43,684 | $41,010 | $38,548 | $36,280 | $34,187 | $32,255 | $30,470 | $28,818 | $27,288 | $25,870 | $24,555 | $23,333 |
| 34 | $48,580 | $45,454 | $42,586 | $39,952 | $37,530 | $35,302 | $33,249 | $31,356 | $29,608 | $27,994 | $26,500 | $25,118 | $23,836 |
| 35 | $50,612 | $47,256 | $44,185 | $41,371 | $38,790 | $36,421 | $34,243 | $32,240 | $30,395 | $28,693 | $27,123 | $25,672 | $24,330 |
| 36 | $52,688 | $49,091 | $45,807 | $42,806 | $40,060 | $37,545 | $35,239 | $33,122 | $31,176 | $29,386 | $27,738 | $26,217 | $24,814 |
| 37 | $54,809 | $50,959 | $47,453 | $44,256 | $41,339 | $38,674 | $36,235 | $34,002 | $31,954 | $30,073 | $28,345 | $26,755 | $25,289 |
| 38 | $56,976 | $52,861 | $49,123 | $45,724 | $42,629 | $39,807 | $37,232 | $34,879 | $32,726 | $30,754 | $28,945 | $27,283 | $25,755 |
| 39 | $59,189 | $54,797 | $50,817 | $47,207 | $43,928 | $40,946 | $38,231 | $35,755 | $33,495 | $31,428 | $29,537 | $27,804 | $26,213 |
| 40 | $61,451 | $56,768 | $52,536 | $48,707 | $45,238 | $42,090 | $39,230 | $36,628 | $34,258 | $32,097 | $30,122 | $28,316 | $26,662 |
| 41 | $63,761 | $58,775 | $54,281 | $50,224 | $46,557 | $43,238 | $40,230 | $37,500 | $35,018 | $32,759 | $30,700 | $28,820 | $27,102 |
| 42 | $66,121 | $60,819 | $56,051 | $51,758 | $47,887 | $44,392 | $41,231 | $38,369 | $35,773 | $33,415 | $31,270 | $29,317 | $27,534 |
| 43 | $68,533 | $62,899 | $57,847 | $53,309 | $49,227 | $45,551 | $42,234 | $39,236 | $36,524 | $34,066 | $31,834 | $29,805 | $27,958 |
| 44 | $70,996 | $65,017 | $59,669 | $54,877 | $50,578 | $46,714 | $43,237 | $40,101 | $37,270 | $34,710 | $32,391 | $30,286 | $28,374 |
| 45 | $73,513 | $67,174 | $61,518 | $56,463 | $51,939 | $47,883 | $44,241 | $40,964 | $38,013 | $35,349 | $32,941 | $30,760 | $28,782 |
| 46 | $76,084 | $69,369 | $63,394 | $58,067 | $53,311 | $49,057 | $45,246 | $41,825 | $38,751 | $35,982 | $33,484 | $31,226 | $29,182 |

## STARTING PORTFOLIO NEEDED TO FUND VARIOUS ANNUAL EXPENSES
### ASSUMING 1% TRUSTEE FEE AND 30% TAX RATE (CONTINUED)

**Inputs**

| | | | | | | | | | | | | | |
|---|---|---|---|---|---|---|---|---|---|---|---|---|---|
| R=real rate of return | 0.0% | 0.5% | 1.0% | 1.5% | 2.0% | 2.5% | 3.0% | 3.5% | 4.0% | 4.5% | 5.0% | 5.5% | 6.0% |
| T=tax rate | 30.0% | | | | | | | | | | | | |
| A=annual admin. fee | 1.0% | | | | | | | | | | | | |
| I=inflation | 4.0% | | | | | | | | | | | | |
| | 1.018 | 1.0215 | 1.025 | 1.0285 | 1.032 | 1.0355 | 1.039 | 1.0425 | 1.046 | 1.0495 | 1.053 | 1.0565 | 1.06 |
| E=expenses to start (ann) | $1,000 | $1,000 | $1,000 | $1,000 | $1,000 | $1,000 | $1,000 | $1,000 | $1,000 | $1,000 | $1,000 | $1,000 | $1,000 |

Figures assume that expenses are all taken out at end of each year.

| Rate of Return (Nominal): Life Expectancies | 4.0% | 4.5% | 5.0% | 5.5% | 6.0% | 6.5% | 7.0% | 7.5% | 8.0% | 8.5% | 9.0% | 9.5% | 10.0% |
|---|---|---|---|---|---|---|---|---|---|---|---|---|---|
| 47 | $78,710 | $71,604 | $65,297 | $59,688 | $54,693 | $50,236 | $46,252 | $42,684 | $39,484 | $36,609 | $34,020 | $31,685 | $29,575 |
| 48 | $81,394 | $73,880 | $67,228 | $61,328 | $56,086 | $51,420 | $47,259 | $43,541 | $40,214 | $37,230 | $34,550 | $32,137 | $29,960 |
| 49 | $84,135 | $76,197 | $69,187 | $62,986 | $57,490 | $52,609 | $48,267 | $44,396 | $40,939 | $37,846 | $35,073 | $32,581 | $30,339 |
| 50 | $86,936 | $78,556 | $71,176 | $64,663 | $58,904 | $53,803 | $49,276 | $45,249 | $41,660 | $38,456 | $35,589 | $33,019 | $30,709 |
| 51 | $89,797 | $80,958 | $73,193 | $66,358 | $60,330 | $55,003 | $50,286 | $46,100 | $42,378 | $39,061 | $36,100 | $33,450 | $31,073 |
| 52 | $92,720 | $83,403 | $75,240 | $68,072 | $61,767 | $56,208 | $51,296 | $46,948 | $43,090 | $39,660 | $36,604 | $33,874 | $31,431 |
| 53 | $95,706 | $85,892 | $77,316 | $69,806 | $63,214 | $57,418 | $52,308 | $47,795 | $43,799 | $40,254 | $37,101 | $34,291 | $31,781 |
| 54 | $98,756 | $88,427 | $79,423 | $71,559 | $64,674 | $58,633 | $53,321 | $48,640 | $44,504 | $40,843 | $37,593 | $34,702 | $32,125 |
| 55 | $101,873 | $91,007 | $81,561 | $73,331 | $66,144 | $59,853 | $54,335 | $49,482 | $45,205 | $41,426 | $38,079 | $35,107 | $32,462 |
| 56 | $105,057 | $93,634 | $83,730 | $75,123 | $67,626 | $61,079 | $55,350 | $50,323 | $45,902 | $42,004 | $38,558 | $35,505 | $32,793 |
| 57 | $108,309 | $96,309 | $85,931 | $76,935 | $69,119 | $62,310 | $56,365 | $51,161 | $46,594 | $42,576 | $39,032 | $35,897 | $33,118 |
| 58 | $111,632 | $99,032 | $88,164 | $78,768 | $70,624 | $63,547 | $57,382 | $51,998 | $47,283 | $43,144 | $39,500 | $36,283 | $33,436 |
| 59 | $115,027 | $101,805 | $90,430 | $80,621 | $72,140 | $64,789 | $58,400 | $52,832 | $47,968 | $43,706 | $39,962 | $36,663 | $33,749 |
| 60 | $118,495 | $104,627 | $92,729 | $82,495 | $73,668 | $66,036 | $59,418 | $53,665 | $48,649 | $44,263 | $40,418 | $37,037 | $34,055 |
| 61 | $122,038 | $107,501 | $95,062 | $84,389 | $75,208 | $67,289 | $60,438 | $54,495 | $49,326 | $44,815 | $40,869 | $37,405 | $34,356 |
| 62 | $125,658 | $110,427 | $97,429 | $86,305 | $76,760 | $68,547 | $61,459 | $55,324 | $49,999 | $45,362 | $41,314 | $37,767 | $34,651 |
| 63 | $129,356 | $113,406 | $99,830 | $88,243 | $78,324 | $69,810 | $62,480 | $56,151 | $50,668 | $45,905 | $41,753 | $38,124 | $34,941 |
| 64 | $133,134 | $116,439 | $102,267 | $90,202 | $79,901 | $71,079 | $63,503 | $56,975 | $51,333 | $46,442 | $42,187 | $38,475 | $35,225 |
| 65 | $136,993 | $119,527 | $104,739 | $92,182 | $81,489 | $72,354 | $64,526 | $57,798 | $51,995 | $46,974 | $42,616 | $38,821 | $35,504 |
| 66 | $140,936 | $122,670 | $107,247 | $94,185 | $83,090 | $73,634 | $65,551 | $58,618 | $52,653 | $47,502 | $43,040 | $39,161 | $35,777 |
| 67 | $144,964 | $125,871 | $109,792 | $96,211 | $84,703 | $74,920 | $66,577 | $59,437 | $53,307 | $48,025 | $43,458 | $39,496 | $36,046 |
| 68 | $149,079 | $129,129 | $112,375 | $98,259 | $86,328 | $76,211 | $67,603 | $60,254 | $53,957 | $48,543 | $43,871 | $39,826 | $36,309 |
| 69 | $153,284 | $132,447 | $114,995 | $100,330 | $87,967 | $77,508 | $68,631 | $61,068 | $54,603 | $49,056 | $44,279 | $40,150 | $36,567 |

**Inputs**

| | |
|---|---|
| R=real rate of return | 0.0% |
| T=tax rate | 30.0% |
| A=annual admin. fee | 1.0% |
| I=inflation | 4.0% |

| | 0.0% | 0.5% | 1.0% | 1.5% | 2.0% | 2.5% | 3.0% | 3.5% | 4.0% | 4.5% | 5.0% | 5.5% | 6.0% |
|---|---|---|---|---|---|---|---|---|---|---|---|---|---|
| | 1.018 | 1.0215 | 1.025 | 1.0285 | 1.032 | 1.0355 | 1.039 | 1.0425 | 1.046 | 1.0495 | 1.053 | 1.0565 | 1.06 |
| E=expenses to start (ann) | $1,000 | $1,000 | $1,000 | $1,000 | $1,000 | $1,000 | $1,000 | $1,000 | $1,000 | $1,000 | $1,000 | $1,000 | $1,000 |

Figures assume that expenses are all taken out at end of each year.

| Rate of Return (Nominal): | 4.0% | 4.5% | 5.0% | 5.5% | 6.0% | 6.5% | 7.0% | 7.5% | 8.0% | 8.5% | 9.0% | 9.5% | 10.0% |
|---|---|---|---|---|---|---|---|---|---|---|---|---|---|
| **Life Expectancies** | | | | | | | | | | | | | |
| 70 | $157,578 | $135,825 | $117,653 | $102,424 | $89,617 | $78,811 | $69,659 | $61,881 | $55,246 | $49,565 | $44,682 | $40,470 | $36,821 |
| 71 | $161,966 | $139,263 | $120,350 | $104,541 | $91,281 | $80,119 | $70,689 | $62,692 | $55,885 | $50,069 | $45,080 | $40,784 | $37,069 |
| 72 | $166,449 | $142,764 | $123,087 | $106,683 | $92,958 | $81,433 | $71,719 | $63,501 | $56,521 | $50,569 | $45,474 | $41,094 | $37,313 |
| 73 | $171,028 | $146,329 | $125,864 | $108,848 | $94,647 | $82,752 | $72,751 | $64,308 | $57,153 | $51,064 | $45,862 | $41,398 | $37,553 |
| 74 | $175,707 | $149,958 | $128,682 | $111,037 | $96,350 | $84,078 | $73,783 | $65,113 | $57,781 | $51,555 | $46,245 | $41,698 | $37,788 |
| 75 | $180,486 | $153,653 | $131,540 | $113,251 | $98,066 | $85,409 | $74,817 | $65,916 | $58,405 | $52,041 | $46,624 | $41,994 | $38,018 |
| 76 | $185,369 | $157,415 | $134,441 | $115,490 | $99,795 | $86,746 | $75,851 | $66,717 | $59,026 | $52,523 | $46,998 | $42,284 | $38,244 |
| 77 | $190,357 | $161,244 | $137,384 | $117,753 | $101,538 | $88,088 | $76,887 | $67,516 | $59,644 | $53,000 | $47,368 | $42,570 | $38,466 |
| 78 | $195,453 | $165,144 | $140,370 | $120,042 | $103,294 | $89,437 | $77,923 | $68,314 | $60,258 | $53,473 | $47,732 | $42,852 | $38,683 |
| 79 | $200,660 | $169,113 | $143,400 | $122,357 | $105,064 | $90,791 | $78,961 | $69,109 | $60,868 | $53,942 | $48,093 | $43,129 | $38,897 |
| 80 | $205,978 | $173,155 | $146,474 | $124,697 | $106,847 | $92,152 | $79,999 | $69,903 | $61,475 | $54,406 | $48,449 | $43,402 | $39,106 |
| 81 | $211,412 | $177,270 | $149,593 | $127,064 | $108,644 | $93,518 | $81,038 | $70,694 | $62,078 | $54,867 | $48,800 | $43,671 | $39,312 |
| 82 | $216,963 | $181,459 | $152,758 | $129,457 | $110,455 | $94,890 | $82,079 | $71,484 | $62,678 | $55,323 | $49,147 | $43,935 | $39,514 |
| 83 | $222,634 | $185,725 | $155,969 | $131,876 | $112,281 | $96,268 | $83,120 | $72,272 | $63,275 | $55,775 | $49,490 | $44,196 | $39,712 |
| 84 | $228,428 | $190,067 | $159,227 | $134,323 | $114,120 | $97,652 | $84,163 | $73,058 | $63,868 | $56,223 | $49,829 | $44,452 | $39,906 |
| 85 | $234,347 | $194,488 | $162,533 | $136,797 | $115,974 | $99,042 | $85,206 | $73,842 | $64,458 | $56,667 | $50,164 | $44,704 | $40,096 |
| 86 | $240,394 | $198,990 | $165,887 | $139,299 | $117,842 | $100,438 | $86,251 | $74,624 | $65,044 | $57,107 | $50,494 | $44,953 | $40,283 |
| 87 | $246,571 | $203,572 | $169,290 | $141,829 | $119,724 | $101,840 | $87,296 | $75,404 | $65,627 | $57,543 | $50,820 | $45,197 | $40,466 |
| 88 | $252,882 | $208,238 | $172,743 | $144,387 | $121,621 | $103,249 | $88,343 | $76,183 | $66,206 | $57,975 | $51,142 | $45,438 | $40,646 |
| 89 | $259,330 | $212,988 | $176,247 | $146,974 | $123,533 | $104,663 | $89,390 | $76,959 | $66,783 | $58,403 | $51,461 | $45,675 | $40,823 |
| 90 | $265,916 | $217,825 | $179,802 | $149,590 | $125,460 | $106,084 | $90,439 | $77,734 | $67,356 | $58,827 | $51,775 | $45,908 | $40,996 |

# Forms for Future Financial Needs Analyses

THE LIFE PLANNING WORKBOOK

# Forms for Future Financial Needs Analyses

I t is advisable that you redo your child's financial needs analysis periodically, because your child's financial needs change over time. Charts One and Two from Part Two of the text should be updated regularly. Additional copies are provided for your convenience. These charts can be used in conjunction with Charts Three, Four and Five from Part Two to calculate your child's needs.

## CHART ONE—PART ONE
## PERSON WITH DISABILITY—MONTHLY INCOME

| Source of Income | Monthly Amount |
|---|---|
| **Employment** | $ _____ |
| **Government Benefits** | $ _____ |
| SSI | $ _____ |
| SSDI | $ _____ |
| Survivors | $ _____ |
| SSA Retirement | $ _____ |
| State | $ _____ |
| County | $ _____ |
| Other | $ _____ |
| **Other Sources** | |
| 1. _____ | $ _____ |
| 2. _____ | $ _____ |
| 3. _____ | $ _____ |
| 4. _____ | $ _____ |
| 5. _____ | $ _____ |
| **Total** | $ |

# CHART ONE—PART TWO

## PERSON WITH DISABILITY—MONTHLY EXPENSES

$ _____ **Housing**

_____ Rent/Month

_____ Utilities

_____ Maintenance

_____ Cleaning Items

_____ Laundry costs

_____ Other

$ _____ **Care Assistance**

_____ Live-in

_____ Respite

_____ Custodial

_____ Guardianship/Advocacy (approx. $50-$75 per hr.)

_____ Other

$ _____ **Food**

_____ Meals, snacks-home

_____ Outside of home

_____ Special foods/ gastric tube

_____ Other

$ _____ **Clothing**

$ _____ **Furniture**

$ _____ **Medical/Dental Care**

_____ General medical/ dental visits

_____ Therapy

_____ Nursing services

_____ Meals of attendants

_____ Evaluations

_____ Transportation

_____ Medications

_____ Other

$ _____ **Insurance**

_____ Medical/Dental

_____ Burial

_____ Car

_____ Housing/Rental

_____ Other

$ _____ **Automobile**

_____ Payments

_____ Gas, Oil, Maintenance

_____ Other

$ _____ **Recreation**

_____ Sports

_____ Special Olympics

_____ Spectator Sports

_____ Vacations

_____ TV/VCR

_____ Summer Camp

_____ Transportation costs

_____ Other

$ _____ **Education, Training, Etc.**

_____ Transportation

_____ Fees

_____ Books

_____ Other

$ _____ **Employment**

_____ Transportation

_____ Workshop fees

_____ Attendant

_____ Training

_____ Other

$ _____ **Personal Needs**

_____ Haircuts, Beauty Shop

_____ Telephone

_____ Cigarettes

_____ Church/Temple Expenses

_____ Hobbies

_____ Books, Magazines, Etc.

_____ Allowance

_____ Other

$ _____ **Special Equipment**

_____ Environmental control

_____ Elevator

_____ Repair of equipment

_____ Computer

_____ Audio books

_____ Ramp

_____ Guide dog/other special animals

_____ Technical instruction

_____ Wheelchair

_____ Other

$ _____ **Total Monthly Expenses**

# PERSON WITH DISABILITY—MONTHLY EXPENSE SUMMARY

## Monthly Expense Summary

1. **Total Monthly Expenses (Chart One—Part Two)**  _____

2. **Total Monthly Income (Chart One—Part One)**  _____

3. **Total Supplementary Funds Required (1 minus 2)**  _____

4. **Reserve in case of Government Benefit Reduction**  _____

5. **Total (3 plus 4)**  _____

# CHART TWO
# FAMILY BALANCE SHEET

| Assets | Joint | Father | Mother |
|---|---|---|---|
| Residence | $ _____ | _____ | _____ |
| Other real estate | $ _____ | _____ | _____ |
| Bank accounts | $ _____ | _____ | _____ |
| Retirement accounts | $ _____ | _____ | _____ |
| CD's | $ _____ | _____ | _____ |
| Annuities | $ _____ | _____ | _____ |
| Stocks, securities | $ _____ | _____ | _____ |
| Business interests | $ _____ | _____ | _____ |
| Other assets | $ _____ | _____ | _____ |

**Liabilities**

| | Joint | Father | Mother |
|---|---|---|---|
| Mortgage debt | $ _____ | _____ | _____ |
| Other debt | $ _____ | _____ | _____ |

**Current Family Net Worth** (current assets less current liabilities)     $ _____

| Life Insurance | Joint | Father | Mother |
|---|---|---|---|
| Death benefit | $ _____ | _____ | _____ |
| Premiums | $ _____ | _____ | _____ |
| Cash value | $ _____ | _____ | _____ |
| **Potential Inheritances** | $ _____ | _____ | _____ |

**Future Expectancies** (death benefits plus inheritances)     $ _____

**Total** (current family net worth plus future expectancies)     $ _____

# CHART ONE—PART ONE
# PERSON WITH DISABILITY—MONTHLY INCOME

| Source of Income | Monthly Amount |
|---|---|
| **Employment** | $ _____ |
| **Government Benefits** | $ _____ |
| SSI | $ _____ |
| SSDI | $ _____ |
| Survivors | $ _____ |
| SSA Retirement | $ _____ |
| State | $ _____ |
| County | $ _____ |
| Other | $ _____ |
| **Other Sources** | |
| 1. _____ | $ _____ |
| 2. _____ | $ _____ |
| 3. _____ | $ _____ |
| 4. _____ | $ _____ |
| 5. _____ | $ _____ |
| **Total** | $ |

# Chart One—Part Two

## Person with Disability—Monthly Expenses

$ _____ **Housing**

_____ Rent/Month

_____ Utilities

_____ Maintenance

_____ Cleaning Items

_____ Laundry costs

_____ Other

$ _____ **Care Assistance**

_____ Live-in

_____ Respite

_____ Custodial

_____ Guardianship/Advocacy (approx. $50-$75 per hr.)

_____ Other

$ _____ **Food**

_____ Meals, snacks-home

_____ Outside of home

_____ Special foods/ gastric tube

_____ Other

$ _____ **Clothing**

$ _____ **Furniture**

$ _____ **Medical/Dental Care**

_____ General medical/ dental visits

_____ Therapy

_____ Nursing services

_____ Meals of attendants

_____ Evaluations

_____ Transportation

_____ Medications

_____ Other

$ _____ **Insurance**

_____ Medical/Dental

_____ Burial

_____ Car

_____ Housing/Rental

_____ Other

$ _____ **Automobile**

_____ Payments

_____ Gas, Oil, Maintenance

_____ Other

$ _____ **Recreation**

_____ Sports

_____ Special Olympics

_____ Spectator Sports

_____ Vacations

_____ TV/VCR

_____ Summer Camp

_____ Transportation costs

_____ Other

$ _____ **Education, Training, Etc.**

_____ Transportation

_____ Fees

_____ Books

_____ Other

$ _____ **Employment**

_____ Transportation

_____ Workshop fees

_____ Attendant

_____ Training

_____ Other

$ _____ **Personal Needs**

_____ Haircuts, Beauty Shop

_____ Telephone

_____ Cigarettes

_____ Church/Temple Expenses

_____ Hobbies

_____ Books, Magazines, Etc.

_____ Allowance

_____ Other

$ _____ **Special Equipment**

_____ Environmental control

_____ Elevator

_____ Repair of equipment

_____ Computer

_____ Audio books

_____ Ramp

_____ Guide dog/other special animals

_____ Technical instruction

_____ Wheelchair

_____ Other

$ _____ **Total Monthly Expenses**

## CHART ONE—PART THREE
## PERSON WITH DISABILITY—MONTHLY EXPENSE SUMMARY

| Monthly Expense Summary | |
|---|---|
| 1. Total Monthly Expenses (Chart One—Part Two) | _____ |
| 2. Total Monthly Income (Chart One—Part One) | _____ |
| 3. Total Supplementary Funds Required (1 minus 2) | _____ |
| 4. Reserve in case of Government Benefit Reduction | _____ |
| 5. Total (3 plus 4) | _____ |

# Chart Two

## Family Balance Sheet

| Assets | Joint | Father | Mother |
|---|---|---|---|
| Residence | $ _____ | _____ | _____ |
| Other real estate | $ _____ | _____ | _____ |
| Bank accounts | $ _____ | _____ | _____ |
| Retirement accounts | $ _____ | _____ | _____ |
| CD's | $ _____ | _____ | _____ |
| Annuities | $ _____ | _____ | _____ |
| Stocks, securities | $ _____ | _____ | _____ |
| Business interests | $ _____ | _____ | _____ |
| Other assets | $ _____ | _____ | _____ |
| **Liabilities** | | | |
| Mortgage debt | $ _____ | _____ | _____ |
| Other debt | $ _____ | _____ | _____ |

**Current Family Net Worth** (current assets less current liabilities)          $ _____

| Life Insurance | Joint | Father | Mother |
|---|---|---|---|
| Death benefit | $ _____ | _____ | _____ |
| Premiums | $ _____ | _____ | _____ |
| Cash value | $ _____ | _____ | _____ |
| **Potential Inheritances** | $ _____ | _____ | _____ |

**Future Expectancies** (death benefits plus inheritances)          $ _____

**Total** (current family net worth plus future expectancies)          $ _____

# CHART ONE—PART ONE

## PERSON WITH DISABILITY—MONTHLY INCOME

| Source of Income | Monthly Amount |
|---|---|
| **Employment** | $ _____ |
| **Government Benefits** | $ _____ |
| SSI | $ _____ |
| SSDI | $ _____ |
| Survivors | $ _____ |
| SSA Retirement | $ _____ |
| State | $ _____ |
| County | $ _____ |
| Other | $ _____ |
| **Other Sources** | |
| 1. _____ | $ _____ |
| 2. _____ | $ _____ |
| 3. _____ | $ _____ |
| 4. _____ | $ _____ |
| 5. _____ | $ _____ |
| **Total** | $ |

# CHART ONE—PART TWO

# PERSON WITH DISABILITY—MONTHLY EXPENSES

$ _____ **Housing**

_____ Rent/Month

_____ Utilities

_____ Maintenance

_____ Cleaning Items

_____ Laundry costs

_____ Other

$ _____ **Care Assistance**

_____ Live-in

_____ Respite

_____ Custodial

_____ Guardianship/Advocacy (approx. $50-$75 per hr.)

_____ Other

$ _____ **Food**

_____ Meals, snacks-home

_____ Outside of home

_____ Special foods/ gastric tube

_____ Other

$ _____ **Clothing**

$ _____ **Furniture**

$ _____ **Medical/Dental Care**

_____ General medical/ dental visits

_____ Therapy

_____ Nursing services

_____ Meals of attendants

_____ Evaluations

_____ Transportation

_____ Medications

_____ Other

$ _____ **Insurance**

_____ Medical/Dental

_____ Burial

_____ Car

_____ Housing/Rental

_____ Other

$ _____ **Automobile**

_____ Payments

_____ Gas, Oil, Maintenance

_____ Other

$ _____ **Recreation**

_____ Sports

_____ Special Olympics

_____ Spectator Sports

_____ Vacations

_____ TV/VCR

_____ Summer Camp

_____ Transportation costs

_____ Other

$ _____ **Education, Training, Etc.**

_____ Transportation

_____ Fees

_____ Books

_____ Other

$ _____ **Employment**

_____ Transportation

_____ Workshop fees

_____ Attendant

_____ Training

_____ Other

$ _____ **Personal Needs**

_____ Haircuts, Beauty Shop

_____ Telephone

_____ Cigarettes

_____ Church/Temple Expenses

_____ Hobbies

_____ Books, Magazines, Etc.

_____ Allowance

_____ Other

$ _____ **Special Equipment**

_____ Environmental control

_____ Elevator

_____ Repair of equipment

_____ Computer

_____ Audio books

_____ Ramp

_____ Guide dog/other special animals

_____ Technical instruction

_____ Wheelchair

_____ Other

$ _____ **Total Monthly Expenses**

## CHART ONE—PART THREE
## PERSON WITH DISABILITY—MONTHLY EXPENSE SUMMARY

| Monthly Expense Summary | |
|---|---|
| 1. Total Monthly Expenses (Chart One—Part Two) | _____ |
| 2. Total Monthly Income (Chart One—Part One) | _____ |
| 3. Total Supplementary Funds Required (1 minus 2) | _____ |
| 4. Reserve in case of Government Benefit Reduction | _____ |
| 5. Total (3 plus 4) | _____ |

# CHART TWO

# FAMILY BALANCE SHEET

| Assets | Joint | Father | Mother |
|---|---|---|---|
| Residence | $ _____ | _____ | _____ |
| Other real estate | $ _____ | _____ | _____ |
| Bank accounts | $ _____ | _____ | _____ |
| Retirement accounts | $ _____ | _____ | _____ |
| CD's | $ _____ | _____ | _____ |
| Annuities | $ _____ | _____ | _____ |
| Stocks, securities | $ _____ | _____ | _____ |
| Business interests | $ _____ | _____ | _____ |
| Other assets | $ _____ | _____ | _____ |
| **Liabilities** | | | |
| Mortgage debt | $ _____ | _____ | _____ |
| Other debt | $ _____ | _____ | _____ |

**Current Family Net Worth** (current assets less current liabilities)  $ _____

| Life Insurance | Joint | Father | Mother |
|---|---|---|---|
| Death benefit | $ _____ | _____ | _____ |
| Premiums | $ _____ | _____ | _____ |
| Cash value | $ _____ | _____ | _____ |
| **Potential Inheritances** | $ _____ | _____ | _____ |

**Future Expectancies** (death benefits plus inheritances)  $ _____

**Total** (current family net worth plus future expectancies)  $ _____

# CHART ONE—PART ONE

# PERSON WITH DISABILITY—MONTHLY INCOME

| Source of Income | Monthly Amount |
|---|---|
| **Employment** | $ _____ |
| **Government Benefits** | $ _____ |
| SSI | $ _____ |
| SSDI | $ _____ |
| Survivors | $ _____ |
| SSA Retirement | $ _____ |
| State | $ _____ |
| County | $ _____ |
| Other | $ _____ |
| **Other Sources** | |
| 1. _____ | $ _____ |
| 2. _____ | $ _____ |
| 3. _____ | $ _____ |
| 4. _____ | $ _____ |
| 5. _____ | $ _____ |
| **Total** | $ |

# Chart One—Part Two

## Person with Disability—Monthly Expenses

$ _____ **Housing**

_____ Rent/Month

_____ Utilities

_____ Maintenance

_____ Cleaning Items

_____ Laundry costs

_____ Other

$ _____ **Care Assistance**

_____ Live-in

_____ Respite

_____ Custodial

_____ Guardianship/Advocacy (approx. $50-$75 per hr.)

_____ Other

$ _____ **Food**

_____ Meals, snacks-home

_____ Outside of home

_____ Special foods/ gastric tube

_____ Other

$ _____ **Clothing**

$ _____ **Furniture**

$ _____ **Medical/Dental Care**

_____ General medical/ dental visits

_____ Therapy

_____ Nursing services

_____ Meals of attendants

_____ Evaluations

_____ Transportation

_____ Medications

_____ Other

$ _____ **Insurance**

_____ Medical/Dental

_____ Burial

_____ Car

_____ Housing/Rental

_____ Other

$ _____ **Automobile**

_____ Payments

_____ Gas, Oil, Maintenance

_____ Other

$ _____ **Recreation**

_____ Sports

_____ Special Olympics

_____ Spectator Sports

_____ Vacations

_____ TV/VCR

_____ Summer Camp

_____ Transportation costs

_____ Other

$ _____ **Education, Training, Etc.**

_____ Transportation

_____ Fees

_____ Books

_____ Other

$ _____ **Employment**

_____ Transportation

_____ Workshop fees

_____ Attendant

_____ Training

_____ Other

$ _____ **Personal Needs**

_____ Haircuts, Beauty Shop

_____ Telephone

_____ Cigarettes

_____ Church/Temple Expenses

_____ Hobbies

_____ Books, Magazines, Etc.

_____ Allowance

_____ Other

$ _____ **Special Equipment**

_____ Environmental control

_____ Elevator

_____ Repair of equipment

_____ Computer

_____ Audio books

_____ Ramp

_____ Guide dog/other special animals

_____ Technical instruction

_____ Wheelchair

_____ Other

$ _____ **Total Monthly Expenses**

## CHART ONE—PART THREE

## PERSON WITH DISABILITY—MONTHLY EXPENSE SUMMARY

| Monthly Expense Summary | |
|---|---|
| 1. Total Monthly Expenses (Chart One—Part Two) | _____ |
| 2. Total Monthly Income (Chart One—Part One) | _____ |
| 3. Total Supplementary Funds Required (1 minus 2) | _____ |
| 4. Reserve in case of Government Benefit Reduction | _____ |
| 5. Total (3 plus 4) | _____ |

# CHART TWO
# FAMILY BALANCE SHEET

| Assets | Joint | Father | Mother |
|---|---|---|---|
| Residence | $ _____ | _____ | _____ |
| Other real estate | $ _____ | _____ | _____ |
| Bank accounts | $ _____ | _____ | _____ |
| Retirement accounts | $ _____ | _____ | _____ |
| CD's | $ _____ | _____ | _____ |
| Annuities | $ _____ | _____ | _____ |
| Stocks, securities | $ _____ | _____ | _____ |
| Business interests | $ _____ | _____ | _____ |
| Other assets | $ _____ | _____ | _____ |
| **Liabilities** | | | |
| Mortgage debt | $ _____ | _____ | _____ |
| Other debt | $ _____ | _____ | _____ |

**Current Family Net Worth** (current assets less current liabilities)　　　　$ _____

| Life Insurance | Joint | Father | Mother |
|---|---|---|---|
| Death benefit | $ _____ | _____ | _____ |
| Premiums | $ _____ | _____ | _____ |
| Cash value | $ _____ | _____ | _____ |
| **Potential Inheritances** | $ _____ | _____ | _____ |

**Future Expectancies** (death benefits plus inheritances)　　　　$ _____

**Total** (current family net worth plus future expectancies)　　　　$ _____

# CHART ONE—PART ONE
## PERSON WITH DISABILITY—MONTHLY INCOME

| Source of Income | Monthly Amount |
|---|---|
| **Employment** | $ _____ |
| **Government Benefits** | $ _____ |
| SSI | $ _____ |
| SSDI | $ _____ |
| Survivors | $ _____ |
| SSA Retirement | $ _____ |
| State | $ _____ |
| County | $ _____ |
| Other | $ _____ |
| **Other Sources** | |
| 1. _____ | $ _____ |
| 2. _____ | $ _____ |
| 3. _____ | $ _____ |
| 4. _____ | $ _____ |
| 5. _____ | $ _____ |
| **Total** | $ |

# CHART ONE—PART TWO

## PERSON WITH DISABILITY—MONTHLY EXPENSES

$ _____ **Housing**

_____ Rent/Month

_____ Utilities

_____ Maintenance

_____ Cleaning Items

_____ Laundry costs

_____ Other

$ _____ **Care Assistance**

_____ Live-in

_____ Respite

_____ Custodial

_____ Guardianship/Advocacy
(approx. $50-$75 per hr.)

_____ Other

$ _____ **Food**

_____ Meals, snacks-home

_____ Outside of home

_____ Special foods/
gastric tube

_____ Other

$ _____ **Clothing**

$ _____ **Furniture**

$ _____ **Medical/Dental Care**

_____ General medical/
dental visits

_____ Therapy

_____ Nursing services

_____ Meals of attendants

_____ Evaluations

_____ Transportation

_____ Medications

_____ Other

$ _____ **Insurance**

_____ Medical/Dental

_____ Burial

_____ Car

_____ Housing/Rental

_____ Other

$ _____ **Automobile**

_____ Payments

_____ Gas, Oil, Maintenance

_____ Other

$ _____ **Recreation**

_____ Sports

_____ Special Olympics

_____ Spectator Sports

_____ Vacations

_____ TV/VCR

_____ Summer Camp

_____ Transportation costs

_____ Other

$ _____ **Education, Training, Etc.**

_____ Transportation

_____ Fees

_____ Books

_____ Other

$ _____ **Employment**

_____ Transportation

_____ Workshop fees

_____ Attendant

_____ Training

_____ Other

$ _____ **Personal Needs**

_____ Haircuts, Beauty Shop

_____ Telephone

_____ Cigarettes

_____ Church/Temple
Expenses

_____ Hobbies

_____ Books, Magazines, Etc.

_____ Allowance

_____ Other

$ _____ **Special Equipment**

_____ Environmental control

_____ Elevator

_____ Repair of equipment

_____ Computer

_____ Audio books

_____ Ramp

_____ Guide dog/other
special animals

_____ Technical instruction

_____ Wheelchair

_____ Other

$ _____ **Total Monthly Expenses**

## CHART ONE—PART THREE
## PERSON WITH DISABILITY—MONTHLY EXPENSE SUMMARY

**Monthly Expense Summary**

1. Total Monthly Expenses (Chart One—Part Two) _____

2. Total Monthly Income (Chart One—Part One) _____

3. Total Supplementary Funds Required (1 minus 2) _____

4. Reserve in case of Government Benefit Reduction _____

5. Total (3 plus 4) _____

# CHART TWO
# FAMILY BALANCE SHEET

| Assets | Joint | Father | Mother |
|---|---|---|---|
| Residence | $ _____ | _____ | _____ |
| Other real estate | $ _____ | _____ | _____ |
| Bank accounts | $ _____ | _____ | _____ |
| Retirement accounts | $ _____ | _____ | _____ |
| CD's | $ _____ | _____ | _____ |
| Annuities | $ _____ | _____ | _____ |
| Stocks, securities | $ _____ | _____ | _____ |
| Business interests | $ _____ | _____ | _____ |
| Other assets | $ _____ | _____ | _____ |
| **Liabilities** | | | |
| Mortgage debt | $ _____ | _____ | _____ |
| Other debt | $ _____ | _____ | _____ |

**Current Family Net Worth** (current assets less current liabilities)          $ _____

| Life Insurance | Joint | Father | Mother |
|---|---|---|---|
| Death benefit | $ _____ | _____ | _____ |
| Premiums | $ _____ | _____ | _____ |
| Cash value | $ _____ | _____ | _____ |
| **Potential Inheritances** | $ _____ | _____ | _____ |

**Future Expectancies** (death benefits plus inheritances)          $ _____

**Total** (current family net worth plus future expectancies)          $ _____

# CHART ONE—PART ONE
## PERSON WITH DISABILITY—MONTHLY INCOME

| Source of Income | Monthly Amount |
|---|---|
| **Employment** | $ _____ |
| **Government Benefits** | $ _____ |
| SSI | $ _____ |
| SSDI | $ _____ |
| Survivors | $ _____ |
| SSA Retirement | $ _____ |
| State | $ _____ |
| County | $ _____ |
| Other | $ _____ |
| **Other Sources** | |
| 1. _____ | $ _____ |
| 2. _____ | $ _____ |
| 3. _____ | $ _____ |
| 4. _____ | $ _____ |
| 5. _____ | $ _____ |
| **Total** | $ |

# CHART ONE—PART TWO
## PERSON WITH DISABILITY—MONTHLY EXPENSES

$ _____ **Housing**

_____ Rent/Month

_____ Utilities

_____ Maintenance

_____ Cleaning Items

_____ Laundry costs

_____ Other

$ _____ **Care Assistance**

_____ Live-in

_____ Respite

_____ Custodial

_____ Guardianship/Advocacy (approx. $50-$75 per hr.)

_____ Other

$ _____ **Food**

_____ Meals, snacks-home

_____ Outside of home

_____ Special foods/ gastric tube

_____ Other

$ _____ **Clothing**

$ _____ **Furniture**

$ _____ **Medical/Dental Care**

_____ General medical/ dental visits

_____ Therapy

_____ Nursing services

_____ Meals of attendants

_____ Evaluations

_____ Transportation

_____ Medications

_____ Other

$ _____ **Insurance**

_____ Medical/Dental

_____ Burial

_____ Car

_____ Housing/Rental

_____ Other

$ _____ **Automobile**

_____ Payments

_____ Gas, Oil, Maintenance

_____ Other

$ _____ **Recreation**

_____ Sports

_____ Special Olympics

_____ Spectator Sports

_____ Vacations

_____ TV/VCR

_____ Summer Camp

_____ Transportation costs

_____ Other

$ _____ **Education, Training, Etc.**

_____ Transportation

_____ Fees

_____ Books

_____ Other

$ _____ **Employment**

_____ Transportation

_____ Workshop fees

_____ Attendant

_____ Training

_____ Other

$ _____ **Personal Needs**

_____ Haircuts, Beauty Shop

_____ Telephone

_____ Cigarettes

_____ Church/Temple Expenses

_____ Hobbies

_____ Books, Magazines, Etc.

_____ Allowance

_____ Other

$ _____ **Special Equipment**

_____ Environmental control

_____ Elevator

_____ Repair of equipment

_____ Computer

_____ Audio books

_____ Ramp

_____ Guide dog/other special animals

_____ Technical instruction

_____ Wheelchair

_____ Other

$ _____ **Total Monthly Expenses**

APPENDIX TWO

# CHART ONE—PART THREE
# PERSON WITH DISABILITY—MONTHLY EXPENSE SUMMARY

| Monthly Expense Summary | |
|---|---|
| 1. Total Monthly Expenses (Chart One—Part Two) | _____ |
| 2. Total Monthly Income (Chart One—Part One) | _____ |
| 3. Total Supplementary Funds Required (1 minus 2) | _____ |
| 4. Reserve in case of Government Benefit Reduction | _____ |
| 5. Total (3 plus 4) | _____ |

# CHART TWO
## FAMILY BALANCE SHEET

| Assets | Joint | Father | Mother |
|---|---|---|---|
| Residence | $ _____ | _____ | _____ |
| Other real estate | $ _____ | _____ | _____ |
| Bank accounts | $ _____ | _____ | _____ |
| Retirement accounts | $ _____ | _____ | _____ |
| CD's | $ _____ | _____ | _____ |
| Annuities | $ _____ | _____ | _____ |
| Stocks, securities | $ _____ | _____ | _____ |
| Business interests | $ _____ | _____ | _____ |
| Other assets | $ _____ | _____ | _____ |
| **Liabilities** | | | |
| Mortgage debt | $ _____ | _____ | _____ |
| Other debt | $ _____ | _____ | _____ |

**Current Family Net Worth** (current assets less current liabilities)          $ _____

| Life Insurance | Joint | Father | Mother |
|---|---|---|---|
| Death benefit | $ _____ | _____ | _____ |
| Premiums | $ _____ | _____ | _____ |
| Cash value | $ _____ | _____ | _____ |
| **Potential Inheritances** | $ _____ | _____ | _____ |

**Future Expectancies** (death benefits plus inheritances)          $ _____

**Total** (current family net worth plus future expectancies)          $ _____

THE LIFE PLANNING WORKBOOK

**To order additional copies of *The Life Planning Workbook* or *Planning For The Future***

## Call (800) 247-6553

**Or complete this form and mail it to:**
American Publishing Company
P.O. Box 988
Evanston, IL 60204-0988

Please send me _____ copies of *The Life Planning Workbook*.    X    $24.95    _____

Please send me _____ copies of *Planning For The Future*.    X    $24.95    _____

Subtotal:    _____

Shipping (first book):    $3.50

Shipping (per additional book):    $1.50

Total Due:

Enclosed is my check for_____.

Please make check payable to American Publishing Company.

Credit card orders, please use our (800) telephone number. Address purchase orders to American Publishing Company. Call for information on bulk orders of ten or more copies.

**Please ship this order to:**

Name _____

Street Address _____

City_____ State _____ Zip _____

Telephone _____